Portrait of Dolls

Carol L. Jacobsen

1. All original Bru   *Burnice Wallen*

To
my daughters

2. The Bye-Lo

ACKNOWLEDGEMENTS

My special thanks to all the collectors who have made possible this second Volume:

Especially to those whose enjoyment of Volume I persuaded me to pursue this exciting task.

And in particular to:

Burnice Wallen who opened her lovely home to me and shared her fine collection of dolls

Ada Odenrider, Ellery Thorpe, Lita Wilson, Rene Harrison and Marian Mosser for their contribution to the Doll Artist section

Lilli Ann Carlstedt, whose dolls are always a delight to photograph and whose home it is always a pleasure to visit

Harriet Livingston whose beautiful dolls add much interest to these pages, both the French dolls and the unusual German bisque

Yvonne Baird who gave considerable time, help and encouragement and offered many of her composition dolls for photographing

Mary Partridge whose contribution to the Modern Doll section in this Volume is most valuable

Roberta Lago whose extensive collection of modern Alexanders has added much interest to this section of the book

Ethel Stewart, who, having contributed significantly toward Volume I, extended further help and encouragement

Ella Dross of the Greenwood Doll Hospital who kindly offered anything helpful from her very special collection

And to the several who wish to remain anonymous but who provided valued information and many special dolls without which Volume II could not have been complete.

3. Aunt Clara, an original by Ada Odenrider

The Author, 1937

A Past and

Present

Portrait of

DOLLS

by

Carol L. Jacobsen

All photographs by the author unless otherwise indicated.

For information concerning the
purchasing of this book write
to the author or to:
S. R. Gill
14851 Jeffrey Road
Irvine, California
92705

Produced by Mandarin Publishers Limited
14 Westlands Road, Quarry Bay, Hong Kong
Printed in Hong Kong

INTRODUCTION

The Portrait of Dolls, Volume II is a Past and Present view of collectible dolls from the 1850's to the present time. In many ways, it is intended to be an extension of Volume I, giving added information and pictures concerning the dolls that appeared in this earlier Volume.

New subjects are discussed in Volume II, among them the American Doll Artist, a subject which has been of interest to a great many collectors. Wax dolls, another type of doll which many are not too familiar with has been presented. Many collectors have expressed a desire to learn more about the Modern Doll of today. These have been discussed at some length at the end of Volume II, bringing into focus the ever continuing story of Past and Present.

The popular French dolls have a good showing in these pages, a number of the Fashion dolls being pictured as well as the French "Bebes".

Throughout the book I have sought to avoid repetition so that those who enjoyed Volume I may find a new and exciting and fresh rendition to add to their library.

The Author

TABLE OF CONTENTS

THE DOLL ARTIST

The American Doll Artist may be well known professionally to collectors everywhere, or may be a homemaker in a small town, turning out her own designs for the satisfaction of herself, her family and her friends. She may make her dolls from start to finish or simply be part of the exciting process. In this chapter I have told the stories of *kinds* of doll artists—from Grace Drayton who only designed dolls to the present day NIADA artists who design and then create their own original dolls.

Marian Mosser has been chosen as an example of one whose hobby of *reproducing* dolls has grown into an exciting and successful business. The story of Kathe Kruse has been included because, while her dolls are of German origin, they have been imported for many years into this country and are much loved by collectors.

Ten years ago the National Institute of American Doll Artists (NIADA) was organized. Those accepted are all high quality artists who have made dolls of their own design. The four NIADA artists chosen here were four I was privileged to work with. There are many others whose work I have personally admired for many years. A good number of these have been pictured in other books and articles. Many of these have become famous and their work is shown in public museums, the Smithsonian Institution among them. Those shown here are a delightful representation of the variety possible, from Ellery Thorpe's child dolls to Lita Wilson's adult portrait of Scarlett.

The late Emma Clear who was known the world over, and beloved, was a real pioneer in reproducing the old dolls. She became known by the many who loved her as "Mama Clear". Having owned a doll hospital for some years prior to the depression, she opened the Humpty Dumpty Doll Hospital in an effort to make ends meet during a difficult financial time. Even in those hard times people came to her doors to have their dolls mended.

The George and Martha Washington which are pictured here are no doubt her best known dolls. They were sculptured by Martha Oathout Ayres. George Washington wears the buckled dress shoes, short, lace trimmed pantaloons and an appropriate suit. He stands behind Martha, his hand on her shoulder.

Martha, perhaps one of the loveliest dolls ever made is of white parian with silver curls and a little lace cap. The hands are a fascinating part of the dolls. The fingers are spread out showing the veins and life lines. It is an interesting sideline to learn that Mrs. Clear was the model for these beautifully detailed hands.

Martha's original costume, shown in the Smithsonian Institution in Washington D.C., has been copied many times for these Clear dolls. The dresses have been entirely hand made and sewn with great care. The Smithsonian keeps on display the lace scarf and purse made by Martha herself and even these have been carefully copied out.

The late Martha Thompson who made such outstanding dolls in bisque and parian will be long remembered for her contributions and admired by other doll artists everywhere.

Originally a portrait photographer, she came easily and naturally into the field of Portrait Dolls, which became her specialty. One of her most outstanding Portraits is Queen Elizabeth II at her coronation.

The two dolls by Martha Thompson that intrigue many are her Prince Charles and Princess Anne. The likeness is done to perfection, and one could never doubt for a moment who the two realistic dolls were intended to be. Princess Anne with her pretty eyes and tiny blonde curls looks as though any moment she might burst into laughter and the play of a small child.

Those who make beautiful reproductions from the past play an important part in the story of doll collecting. A large percentage of collectors will never be able to afford some of the very rare dolls that are the prizes from the past. Such are the Brus, K Star R Pouty dolls, and the favorite French Pouty, S.F.B.J. 252. Polly Mann is one whose beautiful reproductions are given a place of honor by those fortunate enough to own them. Her French Pouty is a favorite in many collections, a lovely interpretation of this rare old doll.

Let us reach into the past again for a moment and bring to light another American Artist who was born in 1877, three years later than Rose O'Neill—Grace G. Drayton. While she did not produce the dolls herself, she designed some of the most delightful composition and rag dolls of her time.

Her drawings, perhaps in part because of the "era" represented are very similar in design to those of Rose O'Neill. The faces are very round, the eyes round, a round curved line for the mouth, more curves at the corners of the mouth making a typical "Drayton" look, a tiny round nose and the suggestion of a curved eyebrow. They often wore big bonnets, simple little dresses which showed their plump dimpled arms and legs. The dolls were very appealing in their time, and remain so to this day. Loveable, huggable, might best describe them.

The Drayton Campbell Kids came into being in the early 1900's to be followed by Bobby Drake and Dolly Drake. Her work between the years of 1900–1925, was accomplished between the ages of 48 and 73.

She designed rag dolls which were charming, loveable to the small fry who held them close to their hearts and dragged them everywhere they went, tucking them under the covers at night where they underwent more tossing and turning through the night hours. Two of these were called Bobbykins and Dolly Dollykins.

Among others, she designed dolls for Horsman, Amberg, Madame Hendren. Dolly Dingle, which came into production between 1923 and 1925 has been a favorite down through the years. This was but one of a large number of character dolls. The names were characteristic of her imagination, names which bring a smile. "Peek-a-Boo", "Hug Me Tight", "Dolly Darling", "Dickie Darling", "September Morn", "Happy Cry".

In 1915 she designed a line of Mother Goose rag dolls which included such characters as "Curly Locks", "Little Red Riding Hood", "Bo-Peep", "Mary and Her Lamb", etc. The costuming in varied colors and design added much to the popularity of these dolls.

The well known Chase Stockinet Doll was made by Martha Chase who began experimenting with her rag dolls in 1889. 1893 was the beginning of her public success when her dolls were accepted by department stores in this country and widely circulated.

See photo 6. The early Chase dolls have a stamped label on the body which reads M.J.C. Stockinet Doll, Patent Applied For. This marking is not found on her later dolls, but the Chase Stockinet name will be found on the head. Her desire was to produce something for children that would be practical. Something that could be washed after much loving, and yet something that would be more than just a simple rag doll. Each one of her dolls was painted by hand, giving the features a look entirely different from the common rag doll.

4. George & Martha Washington
by Emma Clear

5. Queen Elizabeth & Prince Philip
by Grace Lathrop *Burnice Wallen*

6. Chase Stockinet Doll
by M.J. Chase

7. Early Campbell Kid based
on Grace Drayton drawing

Ethel Stewart

8. Polly Mann reproduction of French Pouty

9. The above grouping of an 1874 doll, beautifully costumed, is surrounded with other heads molded by Rene Harrison from the 19th century. *Photograph by Rybiski.*

RENE HARRISON

One of the interesting parts of studying a variety of Doll Artist's Dolls is the discovery that each one is amazingly unique.

It must, indeed, be a thrill to such an artist to design and then create a doll of his or her own making, which in turn, is loved and cherished by many.

While some prefer the child and baby dolls, others lean toward renowned personalities, like some of Rene's work pictured here. Making a doll look realistic would seem an impossible accomplishment to many of us, but making a doll look so much like a famous personage as to be readily recognized, is truly a work of art.

The delightful rendition of a proud great grandmother and baby, which Rene Harrison has called "Golden Years" is but one example of the true to life expressions she has captured in her dolls.

There is a portrait in this face which tells far more than words ever could. The wrinkled brow, the age lines around the eyes which clearly show with the glasses down over the nose. The expression in the eyes captures the twinkle and joy that is being experienced as the old granny cuddles this latest member of her family close to her heart. Rene leaves no question as to what the woman is feeling with this tiny bundle in her arms. Photo 11.

Note the fine costuming detail in the lovely christening gown, the fitting style of the woman's dress, detail of the hands.

As with many of the doll artists, the costuming of dolls is a large part of her work. The research done as well as the hunting out of proper materials and trimmings consumes many hours of time. Rene has made a study of old magazines and books to get the styles of different years, her favorites being the period dolls from 1800 through 1900. She makes these just under 14 inches and finds that they make an impressive grouping in this size.

In photo 9 note the variety of expressions on the faces and the exquisite modeling of the hair.

Some twenty years ago Rene began modeling dolls. The models are made from Roma Italian Plastaline, then the heads produced in porcelain bisque and china painted. They are put together with cloth bodies and authentically dressed, in most cases by Rene herself.

Photo 10 makes an interesting study. Churchill with his snow white cap of hair, the depth of feeling evident in the eyes, the twist to the mouth, wrinkles on the forehead. Even the polka dot bow tie is reminiscent of the old Statesman. The suit is an appropriate glen plaid, complete with vest and pocket chains, tiny button detail. The shirt cuffs show a tiny cuff link.

President Johnson would be recognized anywhere, his face filled with expression, the wrinkled brow, the deep wrinkle under the chin and up into the lower cheek. Again the eyes have a feel to them which convey the personality of the President himself. Rene has made the starched white shirt, the black bow tie, the well fitting dress suit, complete with the miniature white hankerchief showing from the pocket.

A member of NIADA since 1969 Rene has never had any formal training in any phase of doll making. She fell in love with the first reproduction doll she ever saw and started on her own career. She had, however, had experience as a portrait photographer which she feels formed a foundation for the modeling of faces.

10. The two very famous personages represented here are readily apparent. Sir Winston Churchill and President Johnson, modeled in the early years of Mr. Johnson's Presidency. Original by Rene Harrison, *photo by Rybiski*.

11. Golden Years by Rene Harrison   *photo by Rybiski*

12. Scarlett, by Lita Wilson. Costuming by Beulah Brusetti, Australia

LITA WILSON

The exquisite dolls marked "Petite Portraits" are designed by Lita Wilson who has a very special gift when it comes to producing a lifelike figure in porcelain. Lita's early love of dolls led her down the path of creating in her own individual style. Her brief training at the Cleveland Art Institute simply added to her already rare ability to capture likenesses in a breathtaking fashion.

Her Jackie Kennedy doll which took a blue ribbon, demanded many repeat orders. She was produced in four different sizes and in 12 separate versions. The doll is truly a "Portrait", and immediately recognizable to anyone, so exact is the likeness. Over 500 of these were produced and sold.

In addition to the rest of the Kennedy family other notables such as Princess Grace, Prince Rainier, Princess Margaret, have been included in her large family of "Petite Portraits". The sculpturing of the heads no doubt is the most demanding part of the work, though Lita designs in porcelain the limbs which are in themselves a separate work of art. The arms and hands are very realistic, suited in proportion and style to the figure itself, the legs with appropriately designed and molded shoes, or as with Caroline, shoes and sox.

In many cases Lita designs and makes the clothes, authentically fashioned and put together with unusual details. [Her Caroline, for instance, wears a sweet blue cotton frock with tiny daisies embroidered on the yoke, short set-in sleeves and dainty lace trim, complete with underslip.]

Pictured here is her Scarlett, a 20 inch doll of beautiful proportions. Face is full of expression and detail. The long oval face, beautifully formed lips, large green eyes and arched brows all portray the character as she was intended to be. The high cheek-bones, dimpled chin and lovely shoulder design all add to this likeness.

Long brown hair blends beautifully with the soft coloring of the face, the greenish cast of the eyes. Ears are pierced. The slender cloth body is perfectly formed to fit the lovely clothes that are a part of this picture. Legs, from the knee down are porcelain with turquoise green shoes molded on. The shoes have a dainty green bow design suited to the styles of her day.

As might be expected the arms are long and slender, done in

porcelain to just above the elbow. Fingers have beautiful detail with soft pink nails and a bit of pinkish cast to the top of the hand. It is all these tiny details which make an artist doll so realistic.

The clothes are a very important part of this doll, telling well the style of Scarlett's time. First, there are the white pantaloons with a scalloped edge, and tiny white French knots around this edging. They are tied with narrow green ribbon, and two bunches of flowers have been hand embroidered, one on each side. The "bouquet" is a dainty blue for-get-me-not and a tiny pink rose, with dainty minute green leaves.

Over these beautiful pantaloons is a white petticoat trimmed in lace, with a narrow green ribbon woven into the pattern of the lace, tiny tucks and a lovely embroidery that goes across the front panel. This is all in white with tiny white flowers and leaves.

Another petticoat, which has even more detail covers the first one, again with the narrow green ribbon and tiny green bows tied in appropriate places, six rows of tiny tucking. A wide lace panel with green ribbon woven through it comes down each side of the front and on this wide front panel we find more tiny pink roses, hand embroidered, tiny green leaves and little French knots.

After examining all this detail, we come at last to the very beautiful gown which shows well in the photograph. It is a soft white with delicate sprays of pink flowers and soft green leaves, matching well the hand worked underclothes. A ruffled bodice is edged in black velvet, with black velvet ribbon woven through the ruffles. Short sleeves, a green velvet ribbon and green velvet inset at the waistline complete the dress. The straw hat is also trimmed in green velvet.

As might well be expected, Lita is a member of NIADA, her work certainly being deserving of this honor. In addition to the thrill of being able to fashion a true to life model out of clay, Lita says that the greatest rewards to her have been the thrill of meeting many famous personages, coupled with the warm and enduring friendships of others involved in similar lines of work. Most of Lita's production has been in the 60's, but she is hoping to get back into the field of creating her Portraits for those who would so love to add one to their own collection.

ADA BRIDGMAN ODENRIDER

A doll made by Ada Odenrider is certain to be special, whether it be one of her excellent reproductions or a product of her own design. When I visited Mrs. Odenrider she pointed out several shelves filled with her china head reproductions. "Only one of those" she said "is an original. All the rest are my reproductions." I immediately picked out the "old" one and held it in my hand, an expressive turned shoulder head with plump rounded shoulders and a full face, taken from the 1860 period. The initials A.B.O. on the left shoulder proved that I was wrong. This too was a reproduction.

Mrs. Odenrider claims that there is no secret to the way she can turn out a reproduction so beautifully – it is simply the result of careful attention to detail. She has been reproducing china dolls since 1948, and while her preference definitely is china [Probably, she says, because she played with them as a child] she has turned out a fair amount of bisque as well. These include beautiful heads with pale blue eyes, softly tinted cheeks and in some cases, elaborate hair-dos with jewels or other decorations fired and delicately painted. She has made many Brus, reduced to "teenies" as small as $4\frac{1}{2}$ inches.

Among other things, Mrs. Odenrider pays special attention to the eyes. She very much dislikes a doll with flat, expressionless eyes and her work attests to this fact. The "real-life" quality to her dolls is one thing that really stands out. Costuming being her first love, she does not consider a doll finished or complete until she herself has properly dressed it. This is no easy task. In her own book "Wedding Belles" (Published in 1969) she states "Among my earliest memories was my passion for rummaging in family fabric "piece bags" full of scraps left from home dressmaking. A passion, I might add, that I still have with me to this day. Even the smell of the old time dyes was fascinating."

"The nickels given me for candy were spent at the local dry goods or millinery stores for a yard of calico or a few flowers for my dolls. Hours were spent with crayons, scissors, and magazines, cutting out fashion pictures for paper dolls. More hours were spent at Grandma's knee, watching her knit, tat, embroider and crochet."

The doll which took First Prize at the 19th Annual Convention in Seattle, Washington, 1968 is a leading example of her work. Photo 3. It was on the strength of this originally designed doll that she was accepted into the National Institute of American Doll Artists.

"Aunt Clara" as she is named, is a realistic looking Grandmother of a by-gone era, dressed in the style of the 1860's. She sits in a black rocker, measuring 12 inches in a sitting position. The dress is a copy of one of Mrs. Odenrider's very own, one which she wore herself at the Convention. It is a full skirted black taffeta with old black lace edging. A soft grey apron provides a bit of contrast. Underneath are two white petticoats, pantalettes, long black stockings and old leather shoes. She holds on her lap a sewing chatelaine of gold scissors, an emory, a red pincushion, and a needle book. The doll wears a watch chain and an antique gold broach at her neck.

The old hands are weathered looking and full of wrinkles. The head which was made of an unfired composition is covered with silk crepe and beautifully painted. The wrinkles on the forehead, crevices in the cheeks and folds in the throat all give it a portrait quality. The face is painted with pastel powder, brushes and needle for proper effect. Her talent for detail is certainly apparent with this doll. The light in the eyes, the soft grey hairs pulled back into a black snood all create a real life mood.

The Miniature Bridal Salon is another work of art which was on display at the 1972 Regional Convention here in Seattle and merits much comment. Inside an elaborate gold frame lined with white and gold brocade, white velveteen curtains and wine velvet for a rug, stand a group of miniature French Fashions, all reproduced by Mrs. Odenrider. Crystal beads and fish hooks hang from the ceiling making elegant looking chandeliers. A bride model is the center of attention as the prospective customer sits in the salon viewing the various models. She wears a silk taffeta dress which might best be described as "raspberry", a color that really fits no description except that it brings with it a nostalgia from the past. A sales lady stands by the bride-to-be and three other models are to the left. They wear, in turn, a street dress, an afternoon dress and an evening dress. It is impossible to imagine the hours that must have gone into the making of such a display.

In addition to the doll-making and costuming which represent many years of both hard and enjoyable work, Mrs. Odenrider has

13. A bisque head (one of her loveliest) taken from a Greek boy Statuette. Beautiful detail. Expressive blue eyes, soft blue band around hair.

written a charming book which shows her display of forty-five brides. These cover dolls from the period of 1800–1869. She first made the dolls themselves, each with appropriate hair-dos [some molded, some with wigs] and then designed the wedding gowns that show major changes of fashion throughout the years. They are rich in detail from start to finish and one must peruse the book itself to take in the value of this display. It was shown for a long period of time at the Museum of History and Industry here in Seattle.

14. S.F.B.J. 247 "Twirp", a reproduction by Marian Mosser

MARIAN MOSSER

An exciting production is going on in Spring Valley, California and that is the reproducing of beautiful old dolls by Marian Mosser. With an extensive background of making porcelain objects, special lessons in china painting and working for Heirlooms of Tomorrow, Marian took up her interest in dolls in 1968.

Hours of research went into the project, and then the actual experimenting until she had just the perfect bisque for her reproductions. Making excellent molds and choosing the right dolls to make the molds from is not an easy task, but her carefulness in each area of doll making has resulted in a tremendous response from collectors who wish to add her work to their personal collections.

The reproducing of dolls is no mere hobby for Marian. It has rapidly grown into a family project with her husband Bill helping in the doll making, both in the casting of molds from the old dolls and in the actual making of the reproduction dolls.

Marian's mother, Mrs. La Fleur adds her own personal touch to the dolls in the form of costuming. This is a very important part of the whole and the outfits she makes for Marian's dolls are a real addition. Fine human hair wigs are added and when the item is complete, it is a treasure, worthy of being added to a fine collection.

"Twirp" is one of the most popular numbers. She is seen peering out of many glass cases in our area, and has fooled more than one collector who felt sure at first glance that the doll must be an original.

Her tiny Scootles is another favorite, along with Pouty 252, the beloved S.F.B.J. doll.

Many friends have helped by loaning Marian some of the fine old dolls for mold casting. Other times she finds it necessary to purchase a high priced doll, make her mold and then re-sell. Many of the lovely wigs she uses are those she has made herself.

Marian has tried to select dolls who are much wanted by collectors, but too often unavailable or too high priced for them to purchase. In this way, she has made it possible for many to own something very close to the original. Judging by the response and the fact that she has a good three months work waiting for her to complete at any given time, it is evident that she has been accepted as a very special doll maker!

15. Two Kathe Kruse dolls dating to around 1938

KATHE KRUSE

The charming pair of Kathe Kruse dolls on the opposite page measure about 20 inches tall, and are approximately 35 years old.

The two dolls pictured here have human hair which has been rooted in, the legs move and bodies are of pink cloth with an almost plastic like finish. Tickets on their arms read, "Kathe Kruse, Germany".

As a young girl "Kathe" was very poor, certainly too poor to own a fine doll, and with her fertile and imaginative mind she would wander through the trees picking up chestnuts, later to be carved into small dolls. One can easily imagine the little girl, walking along through the autumn leaves, stooping to pick the prettiest of the chestnuts, eagerly gathering them in her arms and bringing them home to carve.

In later years, she chose to marry Max Kruse, a sculptor, who no doubt helped to influence her already creative mind along the line of doll making. When her first child was born, Frau Kruse determined to give her a beautiful doll, one which she made with her own hands. It's success led her on into more and more doll making until at last she was running a factory of her own.

The dolls, which were a fairly new concept at the time were unbreakable, being made entirely of cloth. They were practical also, as they could be washed when too much loving left them dirty and mussed looking.

The heads are a real inspiration, painted in colorful oils with a most lifelike appearance. They seem somehow more like miniature portraits than play dolls, though it was this realistic touch which won the hearts of thousands of children, and which appeals so strongly to collectors today.

Kathe Kruse began working on her first rag doll in 1907 and by 1910 had a new product available for little girls who wanted one to call their own. She not only hand painted the lovely faces, but sewed the clothes, loveable, simple, appealing little outfits. The Kathe Kruse dolls have heart shaped mouths, expressive eyes, button noses and fat little cheeks. They bring to mind in appearance a few of the Schoenhuts, others remind one of the Lenci dolls.

Yet they have an appeal all their own. Frau Kruse had thirteen children of her own, and these dolls stemmed from a strong mother love. She made thirteen different models, one for each of her children.

It is all the more remarkable that this entire family entered into the doll making, helping their mother accomplish this pleasant and rewarding task.

During World War II, Frau Kruse was given orders to close down her factory because Hitler felt her dolls reflected the bewilderment and sorrow of the children who were so eager to purchase them. It is no wonder that she had added a saddened expression to one particular doll, for her youngest child, a son, had been killed in the war.

The war was cruel to Kathe Kruse, taking several of her children in death. She had been given orders to discontinue the doll making which had occupied and thrilled her for many years of her life.

After the war was over she took up doll making again on a smaller scale and soon found that her dolls were making their way into the American stores. This was a tremendous comfort to Frau Kruse, and an encouragement after all the sorrow she had passed through. To find that America still loved and wanted her dolls was indeed a great comfort, and to this day her dolls are being imported into our country. They are selling in our city from $55 for the small 13 inch size. A larger doll sells at $85, and a 21 inch doll, the largest on display here, is priced at $90. The same models are used from year to year but changed by a different outfit, or perhaps a change in hairstyle. Her daughter is now in charge of the factory in Germany.

Recently, while on vacation I stopped along the sea coast to visit a museum which had thousands of dolls on display. Walking up and down the aisles, noticing many lovely dolls, a variety of Bye-Los, the very beautiful K Star R 117, French characters, many many German bisques, and not a few prized compositions, one in particular caught my eye. Standing in the center of the case was a boy, perhaps some 22 inches in height, with eyes so real they caught one's attention, with a sweet pink mouth, a high forehead and a charming little boy's outfit. He stood there looking so real, so special and for just a moment I could not think who had made him. And then, of course, I knew. It could have been no other than Kathe Kruse!

Charlie & Boots, an original by Ada Odenrider

CHARLIE & BOOTS

Charlie represents Ada Odenrider's finest hour. An exact, hand modeled portrait in porcelain of her late husband, friends who knew him well stand in awe at the likeness. As with other examples of her work, this fine artist doesn't stop until the picture is complete. Boots, the little dog who followed Charlie wherever he went, has been added to the scene. He was made with a carved balsa body, with wire to form the shape of the legs, a little red leather tongue, a fur body with soft white on the end of the tail and across the nose. Tiny black headed pins form the eyes and Boots looks up at his master with a very real and loving expression.

"Charlie" is an exquisitely molded portrait with delicate coloring and amazing detail. The cheeks have a faint rosiness to them, the lips a realistic pink and around the chin area is the faintest suggestion of whiskers. His tiny clipped mustache, the deep wrinkles in the neck, the crinkles around the eyes and the deep smile lines forming around the mouth all make him true to life. Even the twinkle in the eye is there.

Charlie (who measures $13\frac{1}{2}$ inches) holds a tiny fishing pole with a miniature reel and fly on the end. A green tackle box is in one hand and a fishing creel (basket) hangs over one shoulder. What catches my eye are Charlie's hands. The tiny fingernails are perfect in detail, the wrinkles which form through the years have been made in a perfect likeness.

The old leather shoes which took an entire day's work look very much the picture of old worn fishing shoes, stretched out of shape a bit from wading in the water, complete with stitching so tiny and perfect one wonders at the patience it took to work out the details of this project. The soles of the shoes were made from Charlie's razor strap.

Because in life Charlie's fishing pants always bagged at the knees, marbles were inserted and the trousers steamed until the proper "bags" appeared. The folds and creases in the clothing all add to the "feel" of the fisherman.

A work of art has been described as that which is produced by skill and taste. Charlie is even more – he is also a work of love.

WAX – THE LUXURY DOLL

She leans against the pillows on a bed, pink rosy cheeks, blonde curls and dress of fine batiste, and someone remarks "She's beautiful!"

A child may look at the same doll and say "Mommy, look at that funny old doll" whereas a husband might remark, "the ugliest thing I've ever seen."

Who is right? And what place does the wax doll have in the collections of today?

As with so many of the collectible dolls, there are wide differences in taste. While a good number of wax dolls are of exquisite beauty and so lifelike as to be startling, a host of them were turned out in homely design, ugly even as they came out of the factory in brand new condition. Others started out as attractive pieces of workmanship, but the melting of wax or damage to the surface has left the doll in a pitifully homely condition.

The doll in picture 16 has an undeniable charm. There *is* a beauty about an old doll like this as one considers the origin (England) and the old ways of doll making which appear here. She is a study from the past and after looking at her for some time there is a delightful little personality which projects itself – no doubt the intent of the original designer.

She was made (many years back before the fine cracks appeared) with a satin smooth face, bright rosy cheeks, a lovely satiny shoulder plate and a dainty neck. The brown eyes are a contrast to the whiteness of the pale flesh tints and they seem to twinkle with a merriment. She reminds me not of a grand lady, but of a young teenager of the late 19th century done up in a summer gown, her blonde curls carefully set for some special occasion. The lips are not set in a serious expression, neither do they really smile. . There is something of the Mona Lisa in her expression—a quizzical, smug little smile as if she were hiding a very special secret.

As I study her further I try to picture her sitting in a fine English home, leaning against a chiffonier or taking her place on a stately bed. I wonder if she sat in a room where red roses twined around a lattice by the window and if, for the owner, doll and roses, and the comforts of home didn't spell a certain little girl security.

The arms bring to mind the fashion dolls with their pink kid and stitched fingers while the body is entirely of cloth. The old, well kept dress is so obviously designed to bring out the coloring in the doll's face that one cannot doubt it was made alone for her. A pale pink underslip shows through the fine white batiste just enough to give the white a pinkish cast. It is tied at the shoulders and at the edge of the sleeves with pink satin bows, and a pink band encircles the waist. Lace edgings, yellow with age, add to the party look of the otherwise plain little gown.

This doll is very easily traced back to the 1840 era when dolls of this type were in vogue. These earlier wax dolls were simple in design, the wax being just a coating over the papier-mache. A well preserved specimen will reveal lovely coloring which was originally painted onto the papier-mache. As the wax coating covered the color, the delicate shades would take on a subtle, realistic toning. These early dolls also were made with a sleeping eye that is controlled by a long wire that fits down inside the body.

The pastel colored kid arms, the cloth bodies with their tiny waists, the corkscrew curls such as those pictured here all date the doll beyond question. An exact duplicate of this particular model has been accurately dated to 1835, though the majority of such dolls began their popularity rise in the 1840's.

Many collectors do not want to bother with wax dolls, for they can be somewhat of a problem. The sun must not beat directly upon them, nor the heat blow too strongly in their direction. A fingernail could ruin the face in an instant, or the carelessness of a small child's play. Having children in the home as often as we do it is rewarding to have dolls about which can be loved and handled by a child, as they were originally meant to be. But one wax doll (photo 17) has found its way into my own collection. She measures 15 inches and is very similar to the doll in photo 18. Both are poured wax, with very attractive cloth bodies with the painted high button boots. The doll in photo 18 has bright red boots, the one in photo 17 a soft purple shade of footwear.

The little wax doll in my collection was made by Cuno & Otto Dressel and the mold dates back to 1884. She has a turned shoulder head, big blue eyes, a sweet closed mouth and her original blonde mohair wig. On her leg is the stamp often found on the Cuno & Otto Dressel dolls which reads Holz-Mazze.

16. Old English wax dating back to 1835

The better wax dolls which run into hundreds of dollars in value today were of poured wax, with inserted hair. In these cases a mold was made of the doll's head, then the wax poured into the mold. The better-made dolls have a thicker wax whereas some poured wax dolls had to be reinforced to keep them from losing their shape. As wax dolls came into popularity many kinds were produced and it was common to cover a composition or papier-mache head with a wax coating. Many times a waxed doll of this nature may be compared to an identical mold in composition which has been left unwaxed.

The poured wax doll has paint over the wax, whereas the waxed over dolls were painted underneath and the color shows through the wax. While the little poured wax doll in photo 17 is of considerable value and a charming little lassie, a doll of this nature cannot begin to compare with the Montanari and Pierotti dolls with their beautiful glass eyes, their finely set brows and lashes, the hairs being set in one at a time, giving a most lifelike appearance. Many of these faces are exquisite and so realistic as to startle one. The warm flesh tones of the wax, the luminous eyes and the detailed lips do indeed form a realistic look. They seem more like little people, than dolls.

The Montanari face is rather serious appearing with a mouth that has a suggestion of turning downward, large expressive eyes, a dainty nose and a rather low forehead. Many times the bodies were made of crude muslin joining the beautiful and detailed wax limbs. The Montanari dolls were introduced at the Great Exhibition of 1851 where they took prizes and a new era of wax dolls began.

A whole new business was booming. As with other styles of dolls through the years, there were many makers, most of them unmarked and it is impossible to trace them all. This new type of wax doll (with the poured wax, set in hair, brows and lashes) had great appeal to the public. While other countries manufactured them also, England was in the lead and the popularity of this luxury item continued until around 1900 when other dolls came into vogue.

One can certainly see why these beautiful dolls with their luminous eyes and elegant design were referred to as luxury dolls. The expense of the doll itself and the fact that many of them seemed almost suitable for royalty made them the prize possession in many a home. Imagine the excitement of a little girl who received such a doll for her very own.

17   18.

Gowns at times were elegant with flounced sleeves, lavishly trimmed in rich laces, scoop necks and fitted waists, skirts that billowed out, sewn with rows of tiny rosettes, and matching hats. Babies wore frilly bonnets and dainty gowns with ribbons tied at the shoulders, or streaming down the folds of the dress.

Another recognized wax maker of this period was Lucy Peck, whose work is still highly prized. Her dolls often had long flowing hair and dainty dresses which show the perfectly formed wax shoulders. The faces show beauty in their design, the eyes of real depth and expression. Her dolls bear a stamp on the cloth body which reads, "Mrs. Lucy Peck, The Doll's House, 131 Regent St., London, W."

As the years rolled on many firms began turning out the less expensive waxed dolls, using papier-mache or composition as a base. The heads on these dolls are also lovely, and well worth collecting. Human hair and mohair wigs were used which could be glued onto the heads and a good many of them have sleep eyes. These dolls were made in large quantity until the turn of the century.

F. G.

The French doll referred to as F.G. is one of the loveliest, and came in a wide variety. From the tiny "F.G." fashion doll with its dainty waist and fine clothing to the large 31 inch bisque headed doll they are much sought after.

In most cases the F.G. doll is easily recognizable with its distinctive features, even though many of them came unmarked. It is most common to find the F.G. marking in a scroll on the back of the head, or the initials F.G. on the corner of the shoulder plate. In some cases a G. only was used and at other times the F.G. was separated with an identifying size number between the two initials.

We know that F. Gaultier made most of these heads, though a Gautier appears to have been on the scene at the time also and may be responsible for some of the F.G.'s.

The Gesland, which so often is found with the F.G. marking on the head should not be confused with the F.G. While Gaultier no doubt made the heads for these Gesland dolls, the Gesland doll is one which stands out by itself, its unusual feature being the fine metal body with the joints, covered with stockinette. This is one of the most wanted French dolls and is usually stamped on the back "Bebe E. Gesland, B.R.E.V.ET S.G.D.G. 5 Rue Beranger 5 PARIS. The legs and arms which were joined to the metal portion of the body were sometimes composition and other times a beautiful bisque with minute detail such as the well rounded toes and fingers, the fingernail detail done to perfection. They should be referred to as the Gesland doll, though because of the F.G. marking on the head, a collector may wrongly refer to them as F.G.'s.

Because Gesland used various initials, among them F. this has caused even wider confusion. It is impossible to always tell just who has made the head, but is generally thought that the Gesland doll with an F.G. head is the same head as those made by F. Gaultier. The Gesland body is of course, of considerably more value than the more common ball joint compostion body, or even the kid body used with so many of the typical F.G. dolls.

The characteristic look of the F.G. is one of arched brows coming close together, a bit differently from the usual Jumeau, an oval face with very full lips.

19. F. G. doll, brown paperweight eyes, brown human hair wig.

20.

21.

22.

23.

13 inch F.G., an unusual child doll, notice beautiful hands.

The F.G.'s were made as early as 1860 and on into 1921, the Gesland dolls from 1914 to 1921. Gaultier made dolls of special character design, colored dolls and gracefully proportioned fashion dolls with their gusset-jointed kid bodies. Photos 20–23 show an unusual child doll with an F.G. marking on the head. The bisque hands resemble those of a Bru, detailed beautifully. She has the large paperweight eyes, the typical F.G. closed mouth and is the tiny enviable size of 13 inches.

It is certain that the F.G. dolls came at least from 13 inches in size to 31 inches. It is always a great deal safer to say what sizes a doll was made in, than what it was not, for rare sizes and models still turn up to amaze and confuse the most studied collectors. The very large 31 inch doll makes a beautiful display. Photo 24 is one such doll, marked F.G. on the shoulder, pale pale bisque of highest quality. There is a full bisque shoulder plate, realistic and beautiful bisque hands, a fine kid body with kid feet. The eyes are a grey-blue, feathered brows, turquoise pendant earrings. She has petticoat after petticoat under her fine gown.

The 26 inch F.G. in photo 28 is another fine example, complete with kid stitched hands, bisque shoulder plate, human hair wig, lovely blue eyes. She is dressed in velvet and satin with an insert of fine lace from an antique wedding gown. Tiny pearls are woven into the lace, originally prepared for a bride of days long past.

The doll in photo 26 sitting, is a Gesland, with the F.G. mark on the head. Her stockinette body is marked with the Gesland markings. She is 24 inches tall, wears old wine–colored French stockings, brownish-red kid shoes with tiny silk bows. Blue eyes. Photo 29, another Gesland with the F.G. in a scroll marking on head, measures 24 inches. Her body, in contrast to photo 26 which is distinctly that of a small child, is more of a teenage modeling. The arms and hands are larger and fuller, like those of a grown child. She has a beautiful body and a fine pale bisque, pierced ears, human hair French wig, brown paperweight eyes. This doll dates to 1860.

At times the F.G. faces seem almost crude, in other instances they are so beautiful one can hardly take one's eyes off them. The French Fashion pictured in photo 30 has no marking, but almost certainly is an F.G. as are a great many of the unmarked French Fashions. Her face is very distinctive looking, almost portrait quality. She has been beautifully dressed to represent the fashions of her era. Beneath

24. 31 inch F. G., exquisite bisque

25. Full faced view of 31 inch F.G.

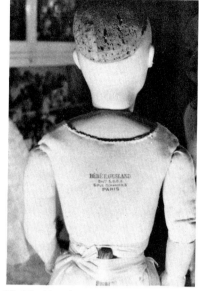

26. Gesland doll

27. Marking found on Gesland body

the voluminous folds of her skirt and petticoats is a tiny pink corset with boning and miniature detail. On her feet she wears antique slippers with tiny heels.

The French Fashion models were, like other top quality French Fashion dolls, exquisitely dressed, many of these costumes being preserved to the present day. Silk dresses of soft blue pin stripes were a common material, often found now in shreds. One such doll has matching tiny heels of the same shade of blue, a dainty hat. A collection limited to F.G.'s alone could be very distinctive, rich in variety and certainly an enviable accomplishment!

28. 26 inch F. G.

29. Large Gesland doll, 24 inches.

30. An unmarked French Fashion almost certainly an F.G. Swivel head.

31. French Fashion marked F.G. in a scroll. 26 inches, almost 28'' measuring to
top of hair. Costumed by Ada Odenrider. Shell pink dress of silk georgette,
appliqued silk flowers.

Burnice Wallen

Bru, all original

Burnice Wallen

The ultimate for many collectors, the fine French Bru, is pictured on page 3 and in color on page 53. She measures 21 inches tall, has brown eyes, the bee sting mouth and all original clothing. Her kid body is in mint condition and she is marked with a circle dot. The color photo shows clearly the delicateness of her bisque, the gentle blending of colors in the softest blue of her dress and the gold trim at the waist, the same shade carried out in the straw of the hat and all blending with the softness of her golden hair. Note the old French stockings and the large rosettes on the French shoes. Black and white photo shows the back of the dress in its fine detail, as well as the design of the large bonnet.

33. Steiner   *Burnice Wallen*

ing her hand in and out of her lovely fur muff. This doll is one of the early mechanicals, dating to 1870.

Designing dolls to play musical instruments seemed to be one of the favorites with the old doll-makers. Some of them, in addition to the already mentioned piano playing, beat drums, and others played violins. It was easy of course to express the appropriate music through the concealed music box. The wonder is that so many of these mechanical dolls work to the present day.

A collector recently displayed for me her rare "swimming doll" a strange looking little creature with arms and legs spread out in the manner of a swimmer and which, when wound, moved its limbs in a swimmer's fashion.

Many of these mechanical items were combined with the old buggies or bicycles of the day. What hours of fun a child must have had with a dolly that could actually push her baby about in a fancy little carriage!

I believe the mechanical that most appeals to me is the very pretty French doll holding a bird cage in her hand. As the music starts to play the little bird hops about as if it were singing. I like to think that perhaps some loving daddy brought this delightful and cheering toy to his daughter's sickroom. It is quite easy to imagine the little girl propped up in bed with pillows, watching by the window, suddenly her lonely little room coming alive with this beautiful child doll and this merry singing bird. It is no wonder that so few of them ever reach public view, for who would ever part with such a prize?

The Little Parisienne (more commonly referred to as the French Fashion) wins the hearts of many collectors today. Often with stitched kid hands, paperweight eyes of a translucent blue, delicately formed features and exquisite clothing, she also came with hats which in themselves were a miniature work of art, carefully lined, covered with silks and satins of the day, perhaps adorned with a soft feather. Kid high button boots, long French stockings, elaborate gowns of varied styles are still in evidence as they turn up with these old dolls. The dainty closed mouths of these dolls add much to the beauty, the soft, often blonde human hair wigs sometimes wound around the heads in an attractive braid.

Magazines of the day provided miniature patterns for these dolls so that children could make additional wardrobes for their Little Parisienne. It is my guess that the mommies had just as much fun with these as their young daughters'.

34. 30 inch long faced Jumeau, dressed in red satin.   *Harriet Livingston*

35. S.F.B.J. mechanical, 20 inches

Harriet Livingston

36. S.F.B.J. mechanical   *Lilli Ann Carlstedt*

37. Jumeau with unusually fine bisque

Burnice Wallen

38. Eden bebe with open mouth, 20", blue eyes.

Burnice Wallen

39. 19 inch Bru, blue eyes, blonde hair, kid body.　　　　　*Harriet Livingston*

40. 33 inch wire eyed Steiner

Harriet Livingston

41. Beautiful French doll marked DEPOSE JUMEAU 11. 23 inches tall.
Dressed in shell pink silk, doll dates to 1886.

42. 24 inch S.F.B.J. 301, original bonnet, human hair wig and original shoes
and sox. *Mary Partridge*

There was a slight crack under the hairline, otherwise the head was perfect. The doll had been in the family, the wife had died and there were no interested surviving children. The price I offered for the doll meant far more to him than the item itself, whereas the doll to me was a real "find".

Today she stands in a glass case in the home of Mary Partridge. In the warm sunshine of early autumn I took the old shredded gown as a pattern and carefully fashioned a duplicate of her original dress in some lovely shell pink satin Mary furnished me. Her original bonnet is still intact, along with her shell pink shoes (marked Paris on the sole) and her own stockings. The markings read S.F.B.J. 301, Paris. Doll is 24 inches.

The most touching experience I have had in searching for old dolls was the acquiring of a very special Schoenhut. In answer to my ad her owner made arrangements for me to see the doll on a specified morning. It was plain to see that she put a tremendous sentimental value on the doll, and, as Schoenhuts are my weakness I feared it would not be possible to meet her price.

When we met and the doll was placed on my lap, it was soon apparent that her description had been quite accurate. A true Schoenhut with label intact, long human hair wig and a finish that was very close to being "mint".

As one can often sense, I could easily see the feeling attached to this little doll – one filled with childhood memories and a deep love for the parents who had given it, plus the obvious fact that it had been well preserved through the years.

The owner, perhaps, could sense just as directly my own attraction to the little doll, plus the "love at first sight" that was spilling over from my ten year old Carrie who was peering over my shoulder and asking, "Can it be mine?"

That moment of silence followed when one is not certain what to offer – and knowing that in a matter of seconds the entire transaction may fall to the ground. Fingering the lovely satin wedding gown which had been fashioned many years ago by the owner's aunt I offered what I felt to be a fair price.

It was not accepted – but instead the doll was placed in my hands as a gift – and one which having come from a total stranger, I shall always cherish.

Kestner Gibson Girl

Perhaps one of the most wanted Kestner dolls is the Gibson girl, shown in color on page 71, and in black and white on the facing page, photo 43. Exquisitely molded with a slender nose and beautiful closed mouth, her hair style and clothing all add to the special feeling that accompanies this doll. She has a kid body with bisque arms and is marked on the head "Made in Germany." Kestner stamped some of these dolls with the name Gibson girl on the body. They date to 1910 and were no doubt produced over a number of years.

Note the very lovely quality of the bisque, the dainty arched brows, the delicate mouth, the large expressive eyes. Doll came with both blue and brown eyes. Appropriately she carries a tiny purse and an umbrella which matches the flowers on her stately hat!

43. 20 inch Gibson girl, brown eyes, copy of original dress.

44. Three "school girls". 36 inch Kestner marked 142, blue eyes, mohair wig. 31 inch Kestner marked 164, blue eyes, blonde hair. Seated, Simon and Halbig, blue eyes, original human hair wig. The two smaller dolls owned by *Mary Partridge*, the 36″ Kestner and school desk belong to *Burnice Wallen*.

74

GERMAN BISQUE

How many times we have all heard the expression, "Oh, it's *just* a German bisque, as if an apology were needed for these delightful dolls.

There are so many variations of the German bisque doll, all the way from the common child doll with its open mouth, ball joint body and mohair wig, to the beautiful K Star R 117 (photo 57).

The German babies with their dimpled cheeks, the Poutys, rare and hard to obtain, and the Kestner Gibson girl are all pictured in this chapter as special examples of what is available in the line of German dolls.

A study of the more common German bisque dolls, along with the very much wanted Hilda's has been included in detail in Volume I. While a few of the more common dolls are shown here, most of the following pictures are intended for the enjoyment of those collectors who may have never seen or owned some of these unusual and valued items.

The K Star R pouty dolls (photos 54, 55, and 56) are favorites everywhere and command high prices. Marie K Star R 101, Peter K Star R 101, Hans K Star R 114, and Hertha K Star R 109 turn up infrequently and remain only briefly on any sales list. The lovely K Star R 117, (photo 57) is perhaps the most wanted of the K Star R dolls.

One of the most special Pouty dolls that has come to my attention was a Marie, perhaps some 9 inches in length. She had been found in an old box with tissue brown with age. The old dress was still on her, the tiny loveable face peeking out from the layer of tissue paper. Her owner was rightfully thrilled over her discovery.

The three dolls in photo 44 are not unusual, but are specimens of good quality and rather outstanding for their large sizes. The doll seated at the old school desk is a Simon & Halbig, the other two are Kestners, the largest measuring 36 inches. She is marked with # 142, the shorter one (measuring 31 inches) is marked # 164. The old school desk is from the Hope School District # 33 of Scotts Bluff County, Nebraska. The owner, Mrs. Wallen, attended this school from 1917–1926. When the little school house and desks were sold the family was able to purchase the desk pictured here, which makes

45. 19 inch doll on left is a Belton, blue eyes, blue dotted swiss dress, closed mouth. Doll on right an unusual closed mouth German doll, 20 inches tall, brown eyes, dressed in coral velvet. *Harriet Livingston*

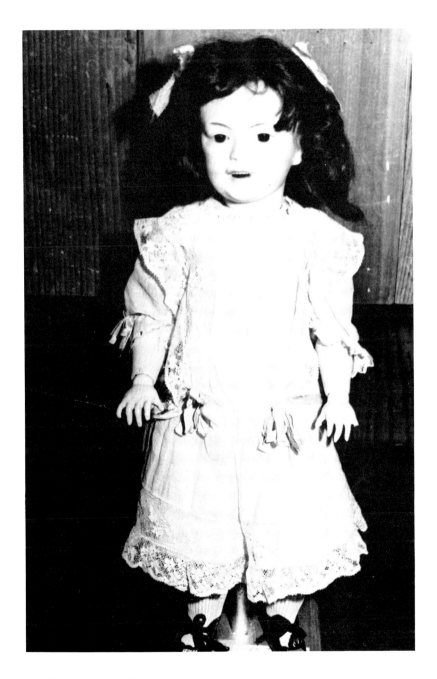

46. Unusual 15 inch German character, brown eyes, original dress. Marked #229.

47. Georgene Averill baby, marked Copr. by Georgene Averill, red molded hair, brown sleep eyes.

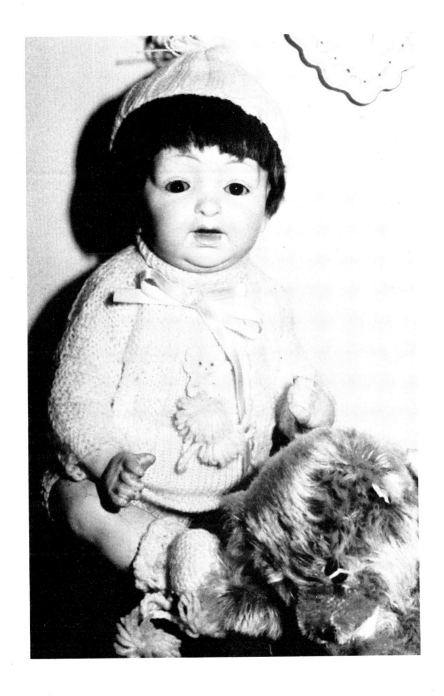

48. 12 inch Kestner baby, marked 211

Harriet Livingston

49. Left to right. Eden Bebe, 19 inches (French) A & M German boy marked 500, 12 inches. Standing behind, the B.S.W. boy known as "Tommy Tucker". 22 inches tall.

Harriet Livingston

50. Very lovely Walkure doll, German bisque. 17″   *Burnice Wallen*

a perfect setting for these larger dolls.

When we think of the more common German bisque, the Florodora, A & M 370, and A & M 390 come to mind. All three of these dolls are still plentiful in supply and easy to buy. This is certainly not to say that they cannot be quite pretty when attractively wigged and dressed.

As collectors become more experienced in the purchasing of dolls, the character dolls begin to have a wider appeal. A choice character doll might well be of a poorer quality than some of the common German bisques, such as the above mentioned A & M numbers. The Heubach dolls, in particular, are not always of a good quality bisque. They are, nonetheless, favorites with collectors. See photo 60 for a good example of a most appealing fellow, who in reality is not a top grade of bisque.

Almost any German made bisque doll with a closed mouth is bound to be special, though these range up and down the scale in value. One German doll that turns up every now and then is a bald head, turned shoulder head, closed mouth, and kid body. This doll is very attractive and if dressed correctly can almost appear of French origin. There are no markings on her shoulder plate or head and it appears that in the 1880's these dolls were sometimes dressed as babies. They give appearance of being a lady doll when one looks at the face. However, they were dressed with baby bonnets and long christening gowns. While a collector might wish to dress them as a child or even a lady doll in some cases, it would be more in keeping with the origin of the doll to display it as a baby, complete with very long christening gown, bows and laces, a snug fitting bonnet and a bit of a mohair wig.

There are a number of German dolls which appear on the market from time to time, similar to the poured wax doll in photo 17. Whether wax, bisque or composition (all three were used) this type of German doll is very appealing. The turned shoulder head, the very lovely sleep eyes, the heart shaped closed mouth and the delicateness of her features make her very special. While Cuno & Otto Dressel designed this particular one, other companies turned out dolls very similar in appearance. This is but one example of a special and appealing closed mouth German doll.

The Simon & Halbig dolls (see chapter 3 in Volume I for additional information and photographs) are many and varied, in most cases of good quality. Almost any doll of this make is collectible. They made many many character dolls, both with open and closed mouths. An entire collection of these would not be unusual and would offer a wide variety of little faces to study.

The tiny Heubach twins in photo 51 are an example of good workmanship. The bisque is of good quality and as one examines them it is hard to believe that such miniature eyes could have ever been set into place. Many of the Heubach dolls do have a good quality of bisque, among them the boy pictured in photo 61. Here we have a closed mouth doll, a very lovely molding of the hair, and the painted eyes. Boy dolls, whether German or French are hard to come by and turn up only occasionally, in comparison to girls and babies.

The unmarked German doll in photo 45 is a real prize. Her face shows a great deal of expression, the mouth is closed, bisque of a fine quality. No one knows who made these dolls, what firm they may have come from. A "sister" doll to photo 45 could well be the open mouth unmarked German doll shown in photo 46. She is quite unusual, a character design and not common.

The Walkure dolls, such as the one shown in photo 50 are nearly always of high quality. The one shown here has lovely brown eyes, a high quality bisque and a very nice ball joint body. She has a string in back, which, when pulled, produces a squeaking noise. The Walkure dolls were made by Kley & Hahn.

One of my favorites among the German dolls is the unusual boy shown in photo 58. He has painted eyes and a closed mouth and reminds one a great deal of the K Star R children, particularly Hans. He is of a top quality bisque, has very detailed and beautiful features. However, he has no marking and his origin is unknown.

The large German bisque dolls, like those in photo 52 (33 inches) and the one on the back cover (36 inches) are grand in action scenes. They make beautiful display dolls in the window of a doll hospital or an antique store. Grouped together around a child's piano, seated at desks or pushing an antique buggy with its parasol top, a smaller German baby lying contentedly inside – all these ideas contribute to realistic displays which are irresistible. The old rockers are ideal for these large dolls, or a group of them might well be set around a little table, covered with an old lace cloth and a valued antique tea set!

51. 7 inch all bisque Heubach twins, tiny sleep eyes, closed mouths marked E.I.
Horsman 1924   *Burnice Wallen*

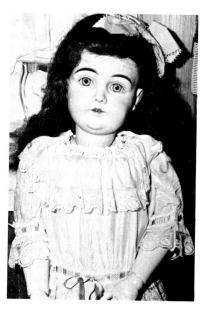

52. Large German bisque doll, 33
inches, marked 146, Germany

53. Turned shoulder head. Dates to
1885.

84

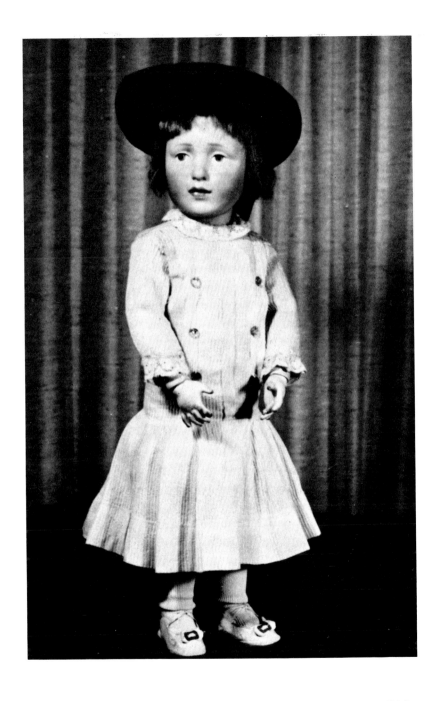

54. K Star R 109, known as Hertha

Burnice Wallen

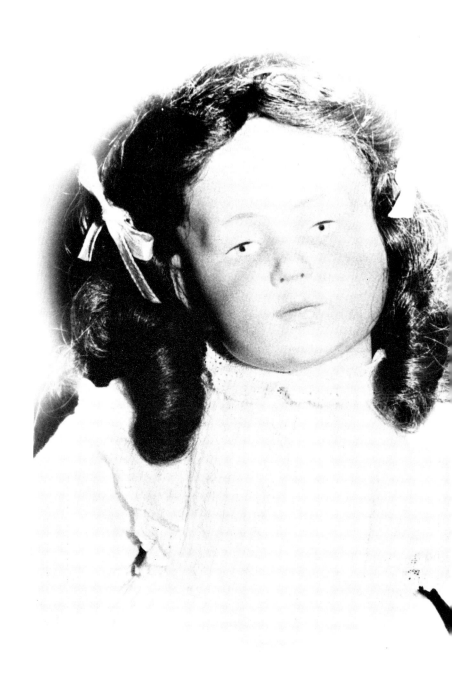

55. K Star R 101—Marie   *Burnice Wallen*

56. K Star R 114—Hans

Harriet Livingston

57. K Star R 117

Harriet Livingston

58. Very unusual German bisque boy, closed mouth, painted eyes, molded hair. No markings. About 14 inches

Ethel Stewart

59. Baby Stuart

THE ART OF PRICING DOLLS

The following Price Guide with accompanying pictures, is intended for use as a Guide, not a final word on the price of any doll represented. In most cases, there is a price "range" indicated, allowing for the many differences which do affect the pricing of every doll.

One major problem with any Price Guide is the tendency of a seller to try and get absolute top price listed therein, regardless of whether the particular doll being offered for sale may be inferior in some way to the one pictured in the Guide. Some dealers, not at all familiar with the doll story feel that a few inches one way or another may not make any significant difference, whereas the size difference may be the very factor which most affects the pricing. This is not always true, but in many many cases the size is of great importance. Neither can one assume that as a doll gets larger, the value should be increased. In many cases the tiniest size of a certain mold is the most valued and sought after by collectors.

At the opposite end of the scale, another fault with Price Guides lies in the fact that an average doll may have been given top price, but a dealer may come up with a doll far above average. One in mint condition, one with a certain hair style, with especially appealing original clothes (or in some cases, beautifully made outfits that are not original) or the fact that such a doll has been in high demand, are all factors that raise the value.

It is wise therefore, to keep in mind the nature of the Guide and to use it as a help, not a final word. Whether buying or selling, a Guide should not be used to manipulate the other party into a corner.

Some of the things which greatly affect the value of a bisque doll (and things which can't be readily seen in a Price Guide) are: The quality of the bisque, (a large variance here) the beauty of the eyes, hair that is worn and matted in contrast to a beautiful head of original human hair in perfect condition, whether the body is entirely original or has hands replaced (or other parts), whether the body has been refinished or is in original condition, the nature of the clothing.

An example comes to mind where an S.F.B.J. turned up with wild looking eyes, cheap quality bisque, an unattractive wig, coloring on the bisque too high, and an inferior body. This doll was priced around $125. The identical mold turned up in a lovely example of French workmanship. This doll had the pearly bisque that is of such high standards, most attractive paperweight eyes of blue-gray, a human hair wig which fell softly below the waist, and was dressed in soft pink velveteen with a pretty hat. The doll sold quickly for $375. Being an open-mouth French doll of excellent quality, this was a fair price.

When it comes to composition dolls, the degree of crazing certainly has a real effect on the value, and once again, the condition of the hair, eyes, clothing and the size. An 11 inch Shirley Temple, for instance, is worth a great deal more than an 18 inch one in equal condition. The same is true of the tiny Scootles which is so sought after by collectors. I think that most collectors would agree that a large factor affecting the value of the composition doll lies in the clothing, which can be very simple (and often in shreds) or quite elaborate with many extras (such as pins, bibs, bonnets, old shoes of special design, accompanying buggies, photographs, storybooks etc.).

The modern doll story is less complicated for there is generally not much wear given to a plastic doll, other than the hair which often can be inexpensively replaced. Here again, the condition of the clothing would be the main factor affecting the value of most of the modern dolls.

60. Unmarked Heubach, open closed mouth. $150–200 *Burnice Wallen*

61. Heubach, closed mouth Molded hair $250–275

PRICE GUIDE

(The Prices which accompany pictures throughout the following Guide have been set by the *author* and are not necessarily the opinion of the person owning the doll pictured.)

BISQUE

BRU, French

15 inch Bru, swivel head, bisque shoulder plate, kid body, paperweight eyes, human hair French wig, beautifully dressed. Begins between $1500 and $2000 and on up depending upon details, beauty of Bru, and demand for the item.

24 inch Bru, same type as listed above. Begins at $1900 and goes considerably higher, depending on factors involved.

Colored Bru, 20 inches, similar to above. Begins at $2500. The demand for such an unusual item is tremendous and makes a specific price in a guide impossible to judge by.

Nursing Bru, kid body, paperweight eyes, etc........ $1300–1500

Paul Girard Bru, bisque head, composition body, closed mouth, dressed .... Begins $1200

FRENCH FASHION
French Fashion, 18–20 inches, good quality, fully dressed, all original, closed mouth, swivel head, bisque shoulder plate, kid body with bisque arms $450–550
French Fashion, similar to above, older model with kid stitched hands, also all original $650–850
French Fashion similar to above with wardrobe, old trunk, miscellaneous items included $900–1100

GAULTIER, (F.G.), French
24 inch F.G., bisque head, composition body, paperweight eyes, closed mouth, good quality, dressed $500–750
F.G. like above, only with open mouth $325–400
F.G., 30 inches, closed mouth, kid body, bisque shoulder head, paperweight eyes, fine quality, dressed $1200–1400
F.G., 13 inches, kid body, closed mouth, original wig, nicely dressed, unusual (see photo 20–23) $850

GESLAND, French
20–24 inch Gesland doll, beautifully dressed, original stamp on body, paperweight eyes, F.G. head .... Begins at $800

HEUBACH, German
Heubach boy, closed mouth, molded hair, painted eyes .. $200–275
Heubach character, open closed mouth, molded teeth ... $150–200
Heubach girl doll, average quality and size, bisque head, ball joint body, sleep eyes, dressed $95–125
Colored Heubach baby, original hair and clothes, 12″ .. $225–275

JUMEAU, French
17–20 inch good quality, open mouth Jumeau, composition French body, paperweight eyes, dressed $275–350
17–20 inch good quality, closed mouth, paperweight eyes, composition French body, dressed $500–650
24 inch closed mouth Jumeau, excellent quality $650–800
12 inch closed mouth Jumeau, good quality, dressed ... $350–425

62. A fine example of a 28 inch Bru, brown paperweight eyes, beautiful bisque, fine kid body, wooden limbs......No price given.

K STAR R (Kammer & Reinhardt, German)

K Star R 101, Marie or Peter, average size $600–750
K Star R 109, Hertha, average size $700–850
K Star R 114, Hans, average size $600–750
K Star R 117, much in demand .... Begins at $750
K Star R baby, 126, 19 inches, dressed $125–175
K Star R girl, 26 inches, flirty eyes, bisque head $185–200
Kaiser Baby, 14 inches, dressed $250–275

KESTNER, German

Baby, common, open mouth, average size, dressed $125–150
Character baby such as #211, 257, 14 inches $175–250
Gibson girl $900–1100
Googlie #221, average size $750–850
Hilda, 13 inches.................................. $300–350
Hilda, 18 inches.................................. $500–650
Hilda, colored, average size $600–850
Kestner girls such as 166, 154, etc. 19 inches $125–150
Kestner girls similar to above, 36 inches.............. $250–275
Oriental #243, 17 inches $750–850

MARSEILLE, Armand, German

A & M 370, 390, 18 inches, dressed $85–90
A & M character baby (not rare) 14 inches, good
  quality $125–175
A & M girl, 28 inches, open mouth, nice quality, ball joint com-
  position body, dressed.......................... $150–200
Dream baby....................................... $85–150
Florodora, 18 inches, all original.................... $95–115

S.F.B.J., French

S.F.B.J. #60, average size $125–200
S.F.B.J. 236, Laughing Jumeau..................... $375–650
S.F.B.J. 247, Twirp............................... $650–850
S.F.B.J. 252, Pouty ....Begins $1850
  This French character child is no doubt at the very top of the list
  of valued character dolls. Price listed above is definitely a bottom
  price – varying factors bringing it up, and up, and up!
S.F.B.J. 301, good quality $250–375

S.F.B.J. 301, all original, good quality, walker type, tosses kiss (not a mechanical) $350–450

S.F.B.J. unmarked, open mouth girl 20 inches, top quality bisque, lovely hair, dressed $250–300

SIMON & HALBIG, German

Colored S & H, #1358, beautiful bisque head, brown composition body $375–450

Jutta, 28 inches, top quality, lovely hair.............. $175–300

Oriental S & H, #1329, dressed $450–600

Rare character dolls, of which Simon & Halbig made many, top quality, average size $250–475

18 inch Simon & Halbig, common but pretty bisque head, ball joint body, nice hair, dressed $125–150

WAX

English wax from 1840, all original clothes, pink kid arms, sleep eyes, original hair, nice condition..................... $250–300

1880 poured wax, nice quality, sleep eyes, wax arms, cloth body, painted high boots, original hair $350–375

MISCELLANEOUS

Averill, Georgene, average size $450–600

Averill, Georgene, large size $650–800

Bye-Lo, 5 inch, all bisque........................ $150–175

Bye-Lo, 10 inch head circumference $175–225

Bye-Lo, 15 inch head circumference $350–425

Here again, there is a difference in the quality of the bisque, some a very fine smooth bisque, others more highly colored. Clothing can add value, at times being very elaborate, long christening gowns, antique bonnets, etc.

Fulper baby, pretty, good quality, 18–20 inches $150–200

Handwerck, 24 inches, good quality, bisque head, composition ball joint body, dressed $135–185

Lori baby, 22 inches, perfect $650–750

Unmarked German bisque, average quality, open mouth, ball joint body, simply dressed, nice hair, around 18 inches...... $65–95

As there is still an abundance of such dolls, their value should not be confused with the better quality dolls and with the rare, expensive numbers.

63. Shirley Temple dolls from Japan
7½, 9 inches. $45 each   *Ethel Stewart*

64. Effanbee doll marked "F" $25
                    Yvonne Baird

COMPOSITION DOLLS

Listed Alphabetically by Make of Doll

ALEXANDER

Alice in Wonderland, early rag doll, dressed $175–185
Alice in Wonderland, 18″ all original $45
Alice in Wonderland, 7 inches, all original $50–55
   Early composition with painted eyes, mohair wig, one piece body.
   Painted shoes & sox, marked Madame Alexander on shoulders.
Baby, 12 to 15 inches all composition $15–20
   These Alexander babies are no special character and usually
   marked on back ALEXANDER in large letters, sleep eyes.
Baby, 16″, cloth body, dressed $25–30
   The popular Alexander baby with closed mouth, big sleep eyes,
   plump cloth body, originally dressed in dress and bonnet.

65. R & B swivel head on shoulder
plate Human hair wig, 18″ $35–45

Yvonne Baird

66. Ideal Mortimer Snerd & Fanny
Brice $50–60

Ethel Stewart

Baby Genius.. $25–30
 The same mold used for Butch, sleep eyes, closed mouth, 12″ the
 most popular size, plump cloth body.
Butch 12 inches, dressed $25
Butch 16 inches, dressed $25–30
Dafoe, Dr., dressed, good condition $55
Dafoe, Dr. with Quint, all original $65–70
Dionne 7½ inches, original $35
Dionne 10 inches, original $35–40
Dionne 15 inches, original $40–45
Dionne 17 inches, original $45
Dionne 19 inches, original $85
Set of 7½ inch Dionnes, dressed $175
Set of 15 inch Dionnes, dressed $185
Set of 17 inch Dionnes, dressed $185–195
Dwarf, all original.......................................$50
Fairy Princess, all original $30

67. 9 inch all composition Wolf, very old, no marks. $35–40   *Ethel Stewart*

68. 15″ Petite Baby, marked "America's Petite Wonder Baby Dolls" $30–40   *Yvonne Baird*

Fairy Queen, all original $30
Greenaway, Kate, all original $45
Henie, Sonja, all original, 14 inches $35–40
Henie, Sonja, all original, 18 inches $55–65
Henie, Sonja, all original, 21 inches $75–85
   Some of the Sonja Henie dolls came in a simple cotton dress which is of less value than the ornate skating costumes, complete with sequins, fur trim, rosebud wreaths, taffeta, velvets, plumes and fine skates.
McFlimsey, Flora, all original, 14 inches $45
McGuffey, Ana, all original, 18 inches $45
O'Brien, Margaret, all original $65–75
   Came in 14, 18, 21 inch sizes, very hard to find doll. Originally with cotton dress, long brown pigtails, sometimes a straw hat.
   Dress label reading Margaret O'Brien, Alexander. Doll is marked with only the Alexander name.
O'Hara, Scarlett, all original, 11 inches $45–50

69. K Star R 114 mold, a Horsman doll. Cloth body. $125

70. Naughty Sue by Horsman $45–50

Ethel Stewart

O'Hara, Scarlett, original dress, coat and bonnet, 18″ $55–65

Snow White, original $50–55
  Snow White is the same mold as Princess Elizabeth and is marked Princess Elizabeth, Alexander on doll. She is different in that she has a closed mouth and a whiter finish to her face, also black mohair wig.

Walker, Jeanne, 14 inches, dressed $35–45

Walker, Jeanne, 18 inches, dressed $45–50

Wedding Party, all original, each $30–35

Wendy Ann, jointed, original dress and hair $50–55

Wendy Ann, 9 inches, painted eyes, not jointed at waist $30

Withers, Jane, early model with closed mouth $85

Withers, Jane, 17 inches, all original, open mouth $75

Withers, Jane, 20 inches, all original, open mouth $75–85
  Very hard to find doll. If dress is missing there is no way to identify her. Green sleep eyes, wig reddish-brown.

 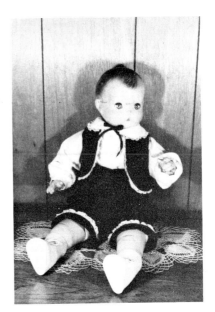

71. 72.

Horsman Brother & Sister. 22 inches. Marked 1937 Horsman. Sister has painted eyes, Brother, sleep eyes. Cloth bodies. $75 each. Dressed in the above picture by Ella Dross of the Greenwood Doll Hospital.

AMBERG

Amberg doll, 8 inches with swivel waist (photo 114) molded hair, painted eyes, marked 1928 . . . . $35–40

Amkid doll with composition head and limbs, 22 inches $25–30

Mibs (see photo 113) $75–85

CAMEO

Giggles (Rose O'Neill) $85

Joy $85

Kewpie (Rose O'Neill) $40–45

Scootles (Rose O'Neill) 18 inches, dressed $50–60

EFFANBEE

American Children (Deewees Cochran) $85–115

These dolls are marked American Children on doll itself.

101

73. Effanbee Rosemary, original wig
$35–40   *Yvonne Baird*

74. Colored Baby Grumpy, Effanbee
Yarn pigtails. $45–55   *Yvonne Baird*

Anne-Shirley, 14 inches, all original $35
Anne-Shirley, 21 inches, all original $40–45
Anne-Shirley, colored, all original $55–60
Anne-Shirley, Effanbee Historical doll, all original $65–75
Anne-Shirley (Actually the Deewees Cochran doll, who is
    often found with an Anne-Shirley mark.) See Volume I, photo
    147 . . . . $90–125
Baby Grumpy, all original $40–45
Bubbles, small size. $25–30
Bubbles, large 22 inch size, all original $55–60
Patsy Family-see section on page 109
Rosemary, dressed. $35–40
Starr, Mae without records $55
Starr, Mae with records, originally dressed $85–90
    Mae Starr dates to 1930, measures 28 inches tall.
Sugar n' Spice, all original, 18 inches $35–40
    Sugar n' Spice is the same mold as Anne-Shirley. Doll is marked

75. 1948 Campbell Kid $50–55

76. Effanbee Baby Grumpy $40–45
Ethel Stewart

only Effanbee, original clothes are marked Sugar n' Spice.
Suzanne, dressed $35

HORSMAN
Baby Dimples, original..............................$25–35
Billiken, good condition $55–60
Campbell Kid, early 1910 model, cloth body, designed by Grace
    Drayton, see photo 7..............................$75–85
Campbell Kid, 1948, Grace Drayton, photo 75 ....$50–55
Cinders, Ella, all original................................$85
    Doll has cloth body, black painted hair, painted eyes, freckles,
    marked 1925 MNS on head. Original cotton dress reads Ella
    Cinders Trademark. Very hard to find.
HEbee SHEbee......................................$50–55
Horsman baby, very old, average size and condition $30–35
Horsman girl, very old, average size and condition $35–40
Jo-Jo...$25–30
K Star R 114, see photo 69 ....$125

77. Horsman Tynie Baby $35

78. Pinnochio (Knickerbocker Toy Co.) $50   *Ella Dross*

Rosebud, 18 inches, dressed.........................$45–50

Tynie Baby, photo 77. In good condition $35–45

A composition version of the Horsman bisque baby made at the time the Bye-Lo was so popular.

IDEAL

Brice, Fanny, Flexy Body (photo 66) $65–70

Durbin, Deanna, 14 inches, all original $35

Durbin, Deanna, 18 inches, all original $50–55

Durbin, Deanna, 21 inches, all original $75–85

Durbin, Deanna, 26 inches, all original $100–125

Garland, Judy, all original, mint cond. $75–85

Ideal girl, almost identical to Deanna Durbin, but marked only Ideal...$40–45

This doll has been reported to have been found in an original box with the Deanna Durbin marking on the box. Face is almost identical to the marked D.D.

Snerd, Mortimer, Flexy Body, Ideal (see photo 66) $65–70

A Past and Present Portrait   *S.F.B.J. 247, Alexander Puddin*

79. 26 inch unmarked doll similar to Rosebud. Human hair wig, top quality $60 *Yvonne Baird*

80. 17 inch unmarked, only fair quality. All original $20. *Yvonne Baird*

IDEAL–SHIRLEY TEMPLE

Temple, Shirley, 11 inches, no clothes \$50–55
Temple, Shirley, 11 inches, all original \$75
Temple, Shirley, 11 inches, original cowgirl outfit \$95
Temple, Shirley, 13 inches, dressed \$45–50
Temple, Shirley, 13 inches, mint condition \$65
Temple, Shirley, 13 inches, flirty eyed, dressed \$75–85
Temple, Shirley, 18 inches, dressed.....................\$50–65
Temple, Shirley, 18 inches, mint.......................\$75–85
Temple, Shirley, 25 inches, all original \$125–135
Temple, Shirley, 27 inches, all original, flirty eyes \$150–185
Temple, Shirley, 27 inches, mint condition \$200–225
Temple, Shirley, 16 inch baby, all original, flirty eyes ...\$125–150
Temple, Shirley, 27 inch, all original baby \$200–225
Temple, Shirley, toddler, rare.......................\$250–275
Temple, Shirley in mint condition, average size IN BOX ..\$85–95

81. 15, 17 inches, Dionnes marked only
Alexander $40–45

82. Alexander Margaret O'Brien all
original. $65–75   *Yvonne Baird*

Temple, Shirley, good condition, with pin, original clothing
    and original Shirley trunk $125–150
    Add per each dress included in trunk (in average cond.)...$5–8
Temple, Shirley, good quality copy, nicely dressed...........$30
    This doll would have an original wig, no markings
Temple, Shirley, poor quality copy, simple dress $15–20
    Grainy composition, mohair wig, poor design

R & B COMPANY (Also known as Arranbee)
Henie, Sonja, 14 inches, all original $25–30
Henie, Sonja, 18 inches, all original $35
Henie, Sonja, 21 inches, all original $35–40
    The above doll was originally dressed in a skating outfit, is of good
    quality composition, a pretty doll with closed mouth, large eyes,
    see Volume I, photo 178
Nancy, 18 inches, all original $35–40

83. 18 inch Shirley Temple, all original
$60   *Burnice Wallen*

84. 16 inch Shirley baby, all original
$150   *Roberta Lago*

MISCELLANEOUS COMPOSITIONS

Bye-Lo, Grace Storey Putnam.........................$50–65

Buddy Lee, dreseed, good condition...................$50–55

Gladdie, good condition, rare $350–375
   Cloth body, came in both bisque and composition. Rosy cheeks,
   blonde molded hair, smiling open mouth.

Hoyer, Mary, all original...............................$35

Mac Arthur, Gen. Douglas..........................$45–50
   All composition doll with uniform. Hat is molded right in with
   composition and he is saluting.

Monica...$55–65
   Came in several sizes, closed mouth, painted eyes, rooted hair.

Raleigh Doll, dates to a beginning of 1918, average condition $85–150

Terri-Lee, all composition $45

Trudy, 3-faced. By Three-In-One Doll Corp. Head turns to 3
   poses, one sleeping, one crying and one smiling...........$65

85. Patsy Ruth, green sleep eyes, blonde human hair wig, dainty old flowered dress of soft pink. Excellent condition. $95–115. *Yvonne Baird*

86. Patsy Joan, original hair, excellent condition. $45–50   *Yvonne Baird*

87. Good quality Patsy copy $35   *Yvonne Baird*

PATSY DOLLS Unless stated otherwise the following dolls are dressed.

Patricia..$45–50
Patsy, very old and hard to find. See photo 137, Vol I........$65
Patsy with painted eyes...............................$25–30
Patsy with sleep eyes.................................$40–45
Patsy Anne, 18 inches................................$35–45
Patsy Baby..$35–40
Patsy Baby-ette $35–40
Patsyette with painted eyes, wardrobe case & clothes.........$65
Patsy Joan $45–50
Patsy Jr. with painted eyes............................$30–35
Patsy Jr. with sleep eyes $35–45
Patsy Lou, 22 inches.................................$50–65
Patsy Lou, unusually appealing outfit, human hair wig, Effanbee bracelet, top condition $85

88. Patsy with sleep eyes, and Wee
Patsy $40–55   *Mary Partridge*

89. Two Patsy Lou's, clothes not
original. $50   *Mary Partridge*

Patsy Mae, 30 inches $95–100
Patsy Ruth, 26 inches..............................$95–115
Patsy, Wee $5\frac{1}{2}$ inches, see photo above................ $50–65
Patsy doll of average size, complete with Patsy trunk and
    clothing $85
Patsy trunk without doll, average size, good condition........$35
Patsy dolls with good human hair wigs, add $5 to their value above
    dolls with molded hair, or missing wigs
Patsy copy, high quality composition, nicely dressed, no marks,
    see photo 87. ....$35
Patsy copy, inferior quality of composition, poor design, simply
    dressed, mohair wig, no markings......................$20
Skippy, all composition $40
Skippy, cloth body with painted shoes and sox, original outfit $50–55
Tinyette, Baby 9 inches $40–45

90. Patricia $45–50

91. Patsy Joan $45

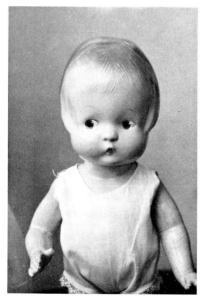

92. Patsy Type $25–30

93. Patsy copy, unmarked $25

94. Patsy with painted eyes $25–30

95. Refinished Patsy $20–25

96. Patsy with sleep eyes $40–45

97. Refinished Patsy $20–25

98. Effanbee Sister and Brother, 12 and 16 inches $20–25 each   *Mary Partridge*

99. Mae Starr Doll $90

Burnice Wallen

100. A modern Kathe Kruse doll. Value new $55

101. Toni Doll by Ideal. All original $25

102. Hard plastic Terri-Lee. Excellent condition $30

103. Alexander hard plastic Jo. All original. $35

104. Saucy Walker $18–20
    Yvonne Baird

105. Alexander hard plastic Peter Pan
    $25–30   *Mary Partridge*

MODERN DOLLS

The following prices of modern dolls apply in general to a doll who has been well preserved. Many times these modern dolls may be found lying in bins with unruly hair, no clothing and stains on the body. Modern dolls in such condition would not in any case approximate the values given here.

Listed Alphabetically by Make of Doll

ALEXANDER

Ballerina, hard plastic, 14 inches, all original $30–35
Cissette, hard plastic (teenage type doll) $15–20
Cissy, 20 inch hard plastic and vinyl, 1955, high heels, original $35
Elise, vinyl, all original $18–20
Lady Churchill, hard plastic, all original. $45–50
Lewis, Sherri, hard plastic, 21 inches, all original. $45–50
Little Women, 14 inches, hard plastic, all original $30–35

106. Dy-Dee baby, rubber ears. $15
Ella Dross

107. 14 inch vinyl Betsy McCall $20
Ella Dross

Maggie, 18 inches, hard plastic, dressed....................$25
Martin, Mary, all original, hard plastic.................$35–40
McGuffey Ana, hard plastic, all original, 14 inches.......$30–35
O'Brien, Margaret, hard plastic, all original, 14 inches....$35–40
Prince Charming, all original, hard plastic..............$40–45
Prince Philip, hard plastic, all original....................$45
Starr, Brenda, 12 inches, vinyl, dressed.................$10–12
Violet, 17 inches, jointed wrists, knees, elbows, dressed....$45–50

AMERICAN CHARACTER
Sweet Sue, 14 inches, hard plastic......................$15–20
Sweet Sue, 20 inches, hard plastic.........................$25
Tiny Tears..$8–10

EFFANBEE
Dy-Dee baby, rubber ears, see photo above..............$12–15

108. Ginny doll complete with trunk and wardrobe $35–40

109. Tiny Tears, all original $10

HORSMAN
Poppins, Mary, see photo 136 . . . . $45
IDEAL
Giggles $12–15
Kissy, all original $12–15
Miss Curity, all original $25
Miss Revlon, 18 inches, hard plastic $25
Tammy, vinyl $3.50
Temple, Shirley, 12 inches, dressed $15–20
Temple, Shirley, 15 inches, dressed $25
Temple, Shirley, 17–19 inches, dressed $30–35
Temple, Shirley, 17–19 inches, dressed, with flirty eyes $35–40
Temple, Shirley, 35 inches, dressed, see photo 110. . . . . $75–80
Toni Doll $15
Toni doll complete with Toni kit, curlers, etc. $25
Walker, Saucy, hard plastic $18–20

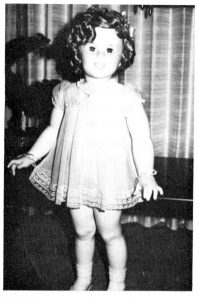 

110. 35 inch vinyl Shirley Temple
$75–80   *Roberta Lago*

111. Chatty Cathys, originally dressed.
$12   *Roberta Lago*

MATTEL

Baby First Step $10
Barbie Dolls no longer available in the stores $5
As above, but with complete costume, excellent condition ..$8–10
Charmin Chatty, no records $5
Charmin Chatty, original outfit, records $17.50–20.00
Charmin Chatty, as above with complete wardrobe....... $30–35
Chatty Cathy, doesn't talk $5
Chatty Cathy, original clothes, talks.................... $10–12
Cheerful Tearful, dressed.............................. $4.50
Singin' Chatty, dressed, sings $12–15

MC CALL CORP

McCall, Betsy, 14 inch vinyl head, hard plastic $30–35
McCall, Betsy, 8 inches, hard plastic, jointed $15–20
McCall, Betsy, as above all original from head to toe...... $20–25
McCall, Betsy, 14 inches, vinyl, dressed $20

112. Cameo's vinyl Miss Peep $20.00

UNEEDA

Pollyanna, all original, see photo 132. ....$40

VOGUE

Ginny, dressed $6.50
Ginny, without clothes $4.50
Jill $10.00

MISCELLANEOUS MODERN DOLLS

Connie Lynn (Terri Lee) hard plastic, dressed $50–55
Jerri-Lee, hard plastic, 16 inches, dressed $35–40
Linda Baby (Terri-Lee) vinyl, molded hair, dressed..........$55
Poor Pitiful Pearl, dressed $12–15
Terri-Lee, hard plastic, 10 inches, dressed...............$35–40
Terri-Lee, hard plastic, 16 inches, dressed $30
Williams, Linda, vinyl, dressed $8–10

Mibs, one of the most loveable of the Amberg dolls, came with a tag, which read, "Love Me, I'm Mibs". Judging by the response of collectors to this piquant little doll, the instructions must have been easy for children to follow. Doll measures 16 inches, reddish blonde molded hair, painted blue eyes, closed mouth.

114.

THE LOUIS AMBERG DOLL

As the "new" type of doll began coming onto the doll market, the "unbreakable" compositions, Amberg took his place among the leading doll makers of his time. While some of these old dolls are homely in design, an amazing number of them are very beautiful and project a great deal of charm.

Pictured above are two very special Amberg dolls, with swivel waists and plump little torsos. The boy has a tag which reads, "Amberg Doll with Body Twist, all, all its own." His shoulders are marked L.A. & S. 1928, the identical marking on the girl. 8 inches.

As with so many of the old dolls, Amberg did not *always* put a trademark on the doll itself, but only on the costume, leaving the collectors of today puzzling over the "possibility" of whether a certain item is really Amberg or not!

One of his much loved dolls was a puzzle to me at the time I wrote Volume I, and appears on page 135 of that book. This is the Amberg Mibs, photo 113 which was made in both composition and bisque, designed by Hazel Drukker in 1921. She has painted sox, little black painted slippers and came with both a wig and painted hair. The piquant expression on her face makes it easy to follow the instructions that came with her. A tag was attached which read "Amberg Dolls, The World Standard, Created by Hazel Drukker, Please Love Me, I'm Mibs".

Very often the initials L. A. S. (Louis Amberg & Sons) will appear on his dolls, or perhaps L A & S with various numbers and the word Germany. More often the marks have been completely worn off, leaving just the faintest rise in the composition, showing that once something was there.

One of the most popular dolls found in today's collections from Amberg are the Happifats. These adorable dolls (boy and girl) have molded clothing, molded hair, molded ribbons in the hair. They are round as little balls and certainly make one laugh to see them with the merry painted eyes and the strange little molded curls coming down sparcely over the fat faces. (Made in bisque and composition.)

Jeno Juszko, a sculptor and doll artist designed over a dozen dolls for Amberg, the Curly Locks doll among them. Grace Drayton was another one chosen to design dolls for Amberg.

Amberg advertised himself as being the largest maker of baby dolls in the world. There were Little Brother and Little Sister, Little Sweetheart, Little Red Riding Hood, Hiawatha the Indian. In addition, he designed dozens of other character dolls. The Education Doll which came out in 1916 had alphabet letters around the skirt. There were walking dolls, crying dolls, adorable little girl dolls with plump ringlets, reminding one of the Shirley Temple era.

The New Born Babe, also designed by Jeno Juszko came out in 1914 and was similar to the A & M Dream Baby. In my opinion this bisque model is very beautiful and certainly looks the part of a tiny infant.

Many of the composition dolls had stuffed bodies and were covered with a pink sateen, where the bisque shoulder plate dolls came with a good quality kid body, copyrighted as AMKID.

As one becomes familiar with the variety of dolls that were for sale during these years, it is fairly easy to spot an Amberg. In the absence of any markings however, one can never be certain unless the doll can be compared to an identical one which has retained its labels, or original markings.

THE SCHOENHUT

One of the most beloved of the true to life child dolls is the Schoenhut, which, as each year of collecting passes, seems to be gaining in popularity.

Between the years 1911 and 1925 a host of variable models and styles were produced, and still turn up in a fair amount, making the addition of such to a collection, not an impossible feat.

As with any good doll there are the rare and hard to find models which carry with them an unbelievably high price. Such is the beautiful doll in picture 115 who wears a painted band around her molded hair. This was one of the earlier Schoenhuts.

During the same era the Schoenhuts were made with molded bows (colored pink or blue) while a still earlier model came with a molded bun. The hair detail is very realistic on these models and the molded hair is preferred to the wigged Schoenhuts.

There is a similarity to the Kathe Kruse dolls found with these Schoenhut children: Certainly both were a new thing on the doll market, realistic, loveable children.

Prior to the dolls which were patented in 1911 Schoenhut made many fine wooden toys, and in 1903 a Humpty Dumpty Circus. In addition to the animals, the circus expanded to include dolls, some of which came with exquisitely designed bisque heads added to an all wood body. Such is the Lady Acrobat. Needless to say, any such item found today is of great value.

His later dolls which most of us are more familiar with were given the name of "All Wood Perfection Art Dolls". The very beautiful oil colors and detail on the faces give them a charming appearance. His original idea of having two holes in the feet, making it possible for the doll to stand was a new concept that appealed to children of all ages. Placed on such a stand, the Schoenhut can take many poses. See photo 117. They can appear to be running, twisting, throwing, tossing, bending. The idea was that a child could have a doll that could do almost anything the child itself could do. Because they were such a popular play doll, many which turn up today are badly scuffed and in need of a bit of repair. Faces are often chipped, and eyes or lips may need retouching.

The Schoenhut baby, photo 118, was made in 1913, and is one of

115. Walt Disney's Ferdinand the Bull with 18 inch Schoenhut, one of the early models with pink band molded around hair. Mint condition, 18 inches.

116. Schoenhut Girl

Burnice Wallen

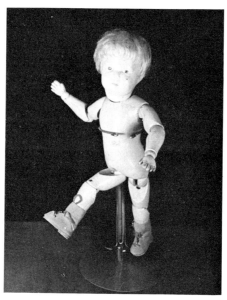

117. Schoenhut

the All Wood Perfection Art Dolls.

Most of the child dolls came in size 14, 16, 17, 19 or 21 inch, a few walking dolls being made in a tiny 11 inch size. This doll is a very collectible item because it differs from the other Schoenhuts in that the limbs are not bendable. It is straight legged and being such a miniature size, most appealing.

The later Schoenhuts were given movable eyes, and most of the later models came with wigs. A Schoenhut is very easy to identify, being the only popular all wood doll produced in this manner. There just wasn't anything else made quite like them, and while the Kathe Kruse dolls have an equal appeal and similarity they are completely different in design and material. The labels, usually still found on the back of the head or shoulders have the year 1911 or 1913 and the name Schoenhut in small print. The words "Schoenhut Doll" with accompanying information is sometimes found imprinted on the shoulders instead of the label.

In addition to the dolls from the Schoenhut Circus, and those with the molded ribbons (or bun) in the hair, the Pouty Schoenhuts are among the most desired. There is an appeal to them that cannot be resisted.

118. Rare bald Schoenhut baby

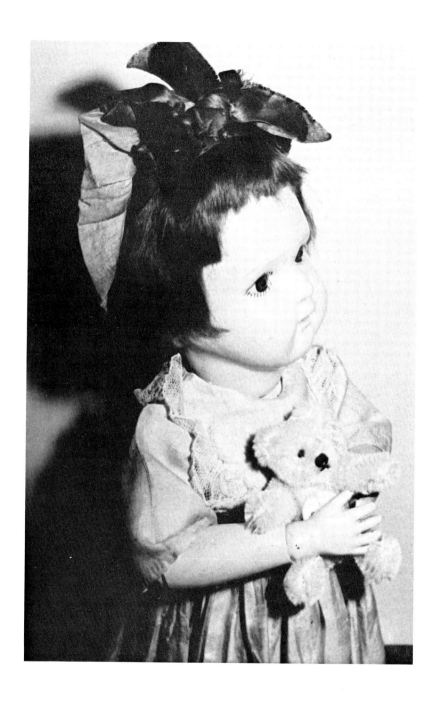

119. 18 inch Schoenhut, all original, brown eyes.

Harriet Livingston

120. Solemn looking little Schoenhut, blue eyes, original mohair wig.

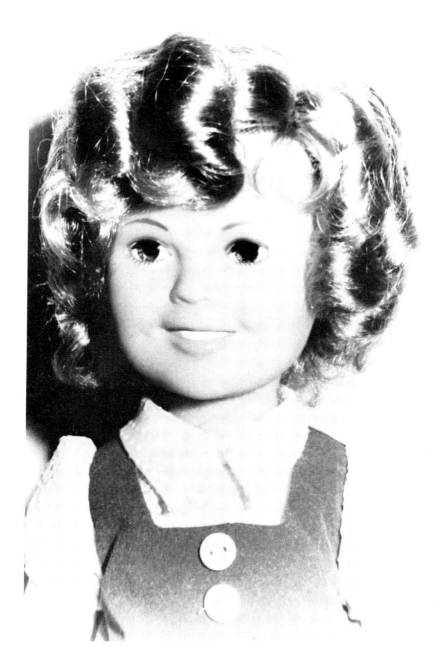

121. 15 inch vinyl Shirley Temple, made in 1972. All original, marked ST-14-B-38

Mary Partridge

THE MODERN PORTRAIT

While there is the natural appeal of something "old" and hard to find in the earlier dolls, the lovely vinyls of today will be the collectibles of tomorrow and many are gathering them up as the new models appear, keeping them fresh and "mint" in the pretty blue Alexander boxes, the Barbie cases or whatever other boxes or trunks may come along with the modern doll.

Of special charm are many of the varied outfits which bespeak the styles of today's little girl. There is a real charm to any collection which follows the trend of doll making down through the years, from the old wooden and wax and china dolls to the lovely bisques, into the celluloids and on down to the composition, the rubber, the hard plastic and now the soft plastics and vinyls which are being made today.

One wonders what new invention may take place that could ever make the present materials seem old, or special to future collectors.

It is my guess that the Barbie Dolls which at times seem to be continually underfoot with our children of today, will one day be most collectible, especially with their rather elaborate wardrobes and accessories. Already several styles have been replaced by newer models and are selling, second hand, quite readily in the neighborhood of $5 per doll.

Certainly most little girls love to grow up and hand down to their daughters the doll they loved most. Such will be the Chatty Cathy's, Ginnys, Pussy Cats and Puddin's of the last few years, just to mention a few.

Going back a bit further, already collectible are the hard plastic dolls, many of which closely resemble the compositions. Alexander made the Little Women and Marmee in hard plastic, Ideal the ever popular Toni doll, complete with kit for giving her a permanent. American Character came out in 1953 with Sweet Sue, a very popular doll. The Dy–Dee doll, Effanbee, was first manufactured in rubber and later made with a hard plastic head.

There was Binnie Walker (Alexander 1954), Violet, a fully jointed hard plastic doll by Alexander, made in 1952, 1953 and 1954. Most collectors are familiar with the Alexander Cissy and Ciscette, with the hard plastic Alice in Wonderland, McGuffey Ana, Margaret O'Brien.

Some of the very popular Ideal dolls of the 1940's include: Pinocchio made in 8, 11 and 20 inch sizes, the Magic Skin Doll, Sparkle Plenty, Baby Coos, Toni. Bonnie Braids, Saucy Walker, Betsy McCall, Miss Curity, Joan Palooka, Miss Revlon followed in the 1950's and the 1960's brought the loveable Thumbelina (a doll with a string in the back, which, when pulled, makes her stretch and move about like a little baby waking up; Kissy (the doll whose lips pucker into a kiss when moved correctly, and at last, Tammy, a runner-up for the Barbie Dolls. Nearly all of these Ideal dolls had some special attraction. The Toni doll, as before mentioned, could be given a permanent. Betsy McCall came with many dress patterns and has proved popular to the present day. The tiny 8 inch size is the most loved and with her jointed legs can be set in cute positions which add to the variety of a collection. Her perky little face brings a smile and her miniature size seems to make her all the more appealing.

Miss Curity came complete with her nurses uniform and a miniature nurses kit. The Revlon doll came with curlers and hair spray, washable hair. A good many of these Ideal dolls were combined with other marketable products (Toni Home Permanent, Revlon Hair Spray, Curity Bandaids, McCall patterns) which increased the public awareness of both the products and the doll. They were highly popular, though the Toni Doll and the Betsy McCall seem to top the list today.

Among the hundreds of plastic dolls that the American public is familiar with, one of the favorites has been the Ginny dolls. The 8 inch Ginny doll was designed in 1948 to be followed with an 8 inch baby sister, named Baby Ginnette, a $10\frac{1}{2}$ inch Jill, a 12 inch Jan and the brother, an $11\frac{1}{2}$ inch Jeff. These were all on the market before 1955. In 1960 a lifelike newborn baby named "Baby Dear", 18 inches long came into the picture. Later in the 60's another Ginny doll, 15 inches tall was designed.

However, it was this little 8 inch Ginny doll that really captured the imagination of the child. She was, to little girls of that time, what the Barbie dolls were to be a few years later on.

Ginny, marked Vogue Doll on the shoulders, has a sweet face with a heart shaped mouth, big blue sleep eyes and soft dainty curls. She has the figure of a small child, plumpish, straight legged. There is good finger detail on the hands, a tiny little nose.

In addition to the convenient small size of the doll, what probably appealed most to the children was the extensive wardrobe offered with Ginny. An original trunk (photo 108) houses over a dozen of these tiny dresses and coats. There is a blue and white sailor dress, a red and white polka dotted dress, several plain lace trimmed cotton frocks, dainty flowered dresses, an adorable gray dress with an inset row of white ruffles with dainty red edging that comes down the side of the shirt, tiny shoes, roller skates, pajamas, straw hats of varied colors to match the clothes.

One of the most collectible of these outfits is the cowgirl set which has a green felt skirt with the imprint of a cowboy riding a horse, a red cotton top with tiny green edging around the neck, matching green boots and green felt panties. A green vest completes the costume. Just as the little girls of today pack their Barbie cases full of clothes, the little girls of yesterday carried with them the Ginny doll, safely stashed away in her trunkful of pretty dresses.

Roberta Lago is one who has beautifully displayed her collection of mint condition, all original "moderns", many of which are shown on the following pages. The majority of these dolls are Alexanders and the clothing is often exquisite. Scarlett O'Hara in a green taffeta outfit complete with bonnet, other character dolls with their velvet vests, tiny gold buttons, frills and laces add a great deal of interest to these dolls.

In the 1960's Alexander put out the Portrait Dolls, among them Renoir, Scarlett, Godey, Melanie, Southern Belle. These are all elegantly dressed and some of them have carried on the character styles that were used with the Alexander hard plastic and composition dolls.

The "American Dolls" by Alexander all have the same faces, measure eight inches in height and are dressed to represent such characters as Hiawatha, Miss U.S.A., Betsy Ross, Amish Girl.

The Madame Doll of 1967, dressed in pink taffeta (see photo 141) has a shamrock on a gold chain and a pearl necklace hidden away in a secret pocket. The idea for this doll was taken from Frances Cavanah's book, "The Secret of Madame Doll".

The Little Women Dolls by Alexander have always been favorites, the four sisters dressed appropriately with Marmee close by in her long gown and pretty dark hair. Laurie has been added with a navy jacket, pin checked trousers and a navy cap. He has the same face as the Little Women dolls.

122. Alice in Wonderland, 8 inches, all original in blue and white   *Roberta Lago*

123. Prince Charming, Alexander, gold brocade, hard plastic. All original.

Mary Partridge

While all the plastic and vinyl dolls would fill a complete book, we cannot pass over the lovely Miss Peep by Cameo (photo 112) one which is still in the stores today, and the abundance of vinyl Kewpie and Scootles dolls. Nor the Ideal Giggles, advertised as "the happiest doll in the world" (1968). She has long saran hair, (photo 134) eyes turn upward, a huge grin. When you press her hands together she cocks her head, rolls her eyes and giggles out loud. She is 18 inches tall, and little girls can have fun shampooing her hair.

Mattel added a host of popular dolls to their name: the Chatty Cathy dolls, Baby Chatty, Charmin' Chatty (complete with wardrobe and a host of records) Shrinkin' Violette, Baby First Step, Cheerful Tearful, all of these for sale in the 60's.

But when we hear the name Mattel we think immediately of the huge and highly successful Barbie family. They had their beginnings in the late 50's and are still being turned out in ever new and imaginative ways. The earlier models are not being made any longer and therefore have become collectors items to a degree already. The 1958 models do not seem nearly as attractive as the later ones. These earlier straight models have been replaced with bendable, living, talking, twisting dolls. Similar to the Chatty Cathy's some of the dolls have miniature records in them and a string which pulls and starts the records going.

A Francie has Growin' hair, a long pony tail which goes back into the head, leaving a short hair-do. There are a variety of Kens, a Stacey, a P.J., Julia, Brad, Christie, Steffie and Miss America.

Two of the cutest models, the Midge with her freckles, and her small sister Scooter are no longer available. Scooter has a sprinkling of freckles, a body identical to Skipper. The clothes are interchangeable, which makes it all more fun.

The large variety of Skippers seems endless. This little sister doll is one of the favorites. The first Skipper was straight legged with long silky hair down her back. A model followed where the knees could be bent, also the elbows. Another model of Skipper was made with a turning waist, and moveable wrists.

Skipper also has hair that can be set, this model called Quick Curl Skipper. One of the cutest Skippers, called Living Skipper, has a little different face, two golden pony tails, long eyelashes and bendable joints.

Alexander Pussy Cats

The Alexander Pussy Cats in color photo on page 141 are in full dress with their pink taffeta coats and matching bonnets. These dolls also come with a soft pink dress, and matching satin slippers, edged in a darling ruffly pink lace. Little white sox complete the picture. Big brown eyes, rosy cheeks and a pink heart shaped mouth add up to a doll that is a favorite with the children of today.

125. Miss America, all original – from the Barbie family.   *Roberta Lago*

145

126. Alexander Sherri Lewis, 20 inches. Gold net over yellow taffeta

127. Alexander hard plastic Lady Churchill – pink

128. Two Alexander hard plastics Prince Philip in black and white

129. 17 inch Leslie, Alexander All dolls on this page from collection of *Mary Partridge*

146

130. Peter Pan dolls, Wendy 13",
Tinkerbelle 9", Michael 13", Peter
Pan 13".   *Roberta Lago*

131. Alexander 21" Renoir Portrait.
Doll in yellow and lace.   *Roberta Lago*

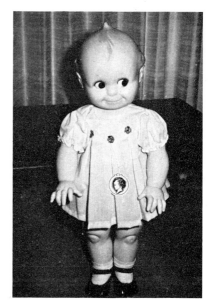

132. Uneeda Pollyanna doll, 31". Red
and white checks, straw hat.
                    Roberta Lago

133. Modern vinyl Kewpie

                    Roberta Lago

134. 18 inch Giggles by Ideal 1966, blue flirty eyes　*Mary Partridge*

135. Love Me Linda by Vogue　*Mary Partridge*

136. 35 inch vinyl Shirley Temple, all original, Ideal 35 inch Horsman Mary Poppins, all original　*Mary Partridge*

137. A fine example of a typical Alexander hard plastic doll. This one has no name or identifying tags. *Mary Partridge*

138. The two 1972 vinyl Shirley Temples, 14 and 15 inches, all original

Mary Partridge

139. 14 inch Alexander Cinderella, vinyl, all original. Pink dress with silver net, crown of pink flowers.   *Roberta Lago*

140. Alexander "Poor Cinderella", green cotton dress, bright orange apron, vinyl,
Roberta Lågo

141. 13 inch Alexander Madame, pink dress and bonnet, vinyl. All original.

Roberta Lago

142. 14 inch Sleeping Beauty, Alexander, gold net over gold, sequin trim. Vinyl, all original.   *Roberta Lago*

143. Alexander Puddin

144., 145. The Alexander Pussy Cat
dolls, one of the most popular of their
modern baby dolls. At right Pussy Cat
wears her original pink taffeta coat
and bonnet, the smaller one wearing a
blue and white check dress. Lower
picture also all original clothing.

146. A scene from "The Good Old Days". The author surrounded by her favorite dolls and her little brother.   1940

THE "GOOD OLD DAYS"

No matter what "era" we grow up in, as we become adults we always look back to our childhood as "The Good Old Days". As I listen to the stories my mother and father tell, the days they grew up in seem far more fascinating than my own.

Each family has its own stories, its own treasures kept through the years, valued not so much for their material, as their sentimental value. Certainly, the collecting of dolls has a large part in this sentimental matter, a doll often reminding one of a grandmother, a mother, or perhaps their own childhood. Having met collectors with varied interests, I still suspect that underneath this fascinating hobby is a strong desire to associate with a past that has long disappeared.

Because of the widespread popularity of doll collecting, and the fact that so many people who aren't collectors seem to be wanting to keep their family dolls, "the good old days" is a term which can well be applied to doll finding itself.

Only a few years ago the Patsys laid in boxes, stacked carelessly in a heap, selling for one dollar, or perhaps a dollar-fifty. I can well remember looking at the pile, most of them needing restringing and thinking that they would never be worth much.

Betsy McCalls were selling for fifty cents, a lovely Rosebud for one dollar, a Shirley Temple considerably less than five dollars.

Every visit to a second hand shop would bring in a pile of these dolls for a few dollars. When refurbished they might sell for twice their original price, but certainly nothing like the prices they are bringing in now, just a few years later.

It was common to find a table with the bisque dolls laid neatly in a row, mostly wigless, but otherwise in pretty good shape, ranging in price from around $14 to $25. There were, of course, a few which brought in higher prices. Even in those days, dealers recognized the rare dolls, the value of the fine French dolls. The prices paid then, which seemed high at the time for these special items, would seem unbelievably small by comparison with today's market.

Collectors seem to enjoy talking about these days, as the good old days, on the one hand blaming themselves time and again for the bargains passed up, other times showing a favoured doll that was purchased "then" and sits in a place of honor today.

147. Two lovely dolls of composition. The doll on the left is unmarked, dressed in original dress of pink with green satin bands, the one on the right a Rosebud, dressed in soft orange. Such dolls, once for sale in second hand stores for one or two dollars, are now selling for high prices.

Carrie Jacobsen with large Simon & Halbig doll

Echoes of the past in color photo on page 159. Carrie, now ten years old looks at a life size Simon & Halbig, Heinrich Handwerck doll that measures 36 inches high. Old lace and roses gracefully form a draping over her shoulders, a tiny photograph on the dresser reminds the owner of her own little girl who is now a mother herself. A variety of colorful, smaller dolls are housed in the glass cupboards in the background.

148.

For myself, the good old days involved many hours of play with the dolls shown in photo 148. My little brother and I would often make a doll hospital out of our furnished basement, complete with sick beds, thermometers, candy pills, warm blankets. He was the doctor with a fancy kit, while I became nurse administering the candy pills (most of which we quickly swallowed). Playing bride and groom was another pastime, the bride shown here in full dress, with a bridesmaid on either side.

The above picture was taken by my father, no doubt in deference to my pleas. One bright Saturday morning we set the dolls up on the side rockery and posed them in their best clothes. Then on Sunday morning I would take them all, or nearly all of them to Sunday School with me and line them up on the back seat of the car. At last the sad day came when my father said to me, "Carol, I think you are old enough now to just take one doll with you when you go to Sunday School!"

The bride doll in the center front was my favorite, and has since been identified as "Jo-Jo", by Horsman. On either side of her are two all original Alexander dolls.

The others, long gone, are not known to me and were perhaps unmarked dolls. The one at the left wears an original blue and white taffeta outfit. She was purchased in 1938. Beside her a small baby wears an original dress and bonnet of soft pink.

In contrast to the dolls of my time, it is most interesting to go back, through the help of the old catalogs, to the closing years of the nineteenth century and the early years of the 20th century and compare prices with those of today. Of course it is easy to forget that all prices were much lower during those days so that by comparison, some of the dolls were actually high priced.

In 1892 the Bebe Steiner was advertised at $90.00 a dozen, (18 inch size). These dolls were beautifully dressed with fancy bonnets, decorative ribbon, long flowing hair, and embroidered dresses. Such a thing seems impossible to believe with present values.

China dolls ran 75 cents a dozen, French bisque heads began around $5.00 a dozen. The much prized (today) bronzed leather slippers with rosette trimming, and the fancy hats sold around fifteen cents a piece.

It is rather interesting to go through these old catalogs and try and guess what make of doll might have been offered. In some instances, as with Steiner and Jumeau the firm names were given. Other times the dolls were simply advertised with the name of the company who was selling them such as Marshall Field or Montgomery Ward, or Butler Brothers, among others.

In 1892 the Bebe Jumeau was sold for $1.50. She was dressed lavishly, sometimes with lace panels down the front of her gown, tucking, pleats, satin ribbons, elegant bonnets, matching shoes.

Even a 26 inch Jumeau sold for $6.50, a 35 inch one for $15.00. Trying to reconstruct the prices of that time, it is easier to see how a $15.00 doll would have been considered very expensive to a family of that time. Even today, a $15.00 doll, purchased for a child, would not be considered cheap. Such a doll in 1892 must have been kept as a very special plaything, something mostly to be set in the corner of the room, and looked at. This could explain why so many of them have been well preserved to the present day.

It is also easy to see why, with the coming of the next century and the real play dolls, the Schoenhut, the "Can't Break ems" and the other variety of compositions coming onto the market, little girls

162

thrilled to the opportunity of having something they could really play with. To be able to tuck a dolly in bed, take it outdoors to play, this was a whole new delight.

In 1895 the ads were full of dress descriptions which must have thrilled the little girls scanning the pages. A "29 inch bisque doll dressed in pale blue moire silk, tiny tucks, lace ruching, patent shoes, flounces, lace trimmed muslin underwear" etc. all made sense to the child of that day. These were the clothes mother wore. The child of today wouldn't begin to know the meaning of such a description. Leg o'mutton sleeves, ostrich feathers, slippers with buckles, corded trimming, velvet capes and bronzed leather slippers were all the style of the hour.

China dolls were selling for 30 cents a dozen, frozen Charlottes at 24 cents a dozen. A 34 inch wax doll with flowing hair sold for one dollar. Some of the china dolls were advertised as being "well worth 5 cents". 1895 brought the 23 inch Lily Langtry doll dressed in yellow satin, lace, undies, and real stockings, with a big hat, all for $5.25. As one reads through the ads they seem to be in exciting competition, each doll a little bigger and a little better than the one listed before.

A 10 cent assortment of tiny French bisque dolls certainly sounds exciting. Doll carriages now highly prized sold at $10.50 a dozen. Some of these had parasols attached, fancy curving handles, wicker frames.

1895 also brought advertisements of French baby dolls with fancy baby caps and long dresses, 11 inches in size, $1.98 a dozen.

There are no doubt several reasons why these dolls were not purchased in quantity. The most obvious of course, is the fact that the prices were in accord with other prices of the day. Just as the mothers today cannot usually afford to go into a store and buy up a large assortment of better dolls, the mothers of that time probably did well to purchase one nice doll for their daughter. And even if the family was very well to do, there was not the interest at that time in doll collecting that we have today.

Before the 1850's most little girls were content with a rag doll or some item that had to be very carefully kept, just to be looked at. The era of the play doll had not arrived. So that the thought of them ever being of value as an antique, or a collector's item probably never entered the minds of even the most wealthy. Today collectors are aware that with the passing of just a few years, even a plastic doll will have a collectible value if it is a good item to begin with.

As we follow the ads into the 1900's we find the composition dolls coming into vogue, their ringlets tied in pretty bows, dolls dressed with kindergarten picture borders and pretty collars. The word unbreakable appears many times in these pages, though we find the compositions still mixed with the bisques. The old era was fading and a new one was taking over, but for some years there was a mixture of two, many who held to the old bisque dolls and were hesitant to branch out to the newer compositions. Gradually, the practicality of the latter took over. Sailor costumes were in style, sometimes a boy and girl doll being dressed alike in these outfits.

In 1914 the celluloid dolls were advertised, and in 1919 we find the Kewpie ads, the ever popular Kewpies dressed with short full skirts and huge bonnets.

The Kestner character baby dolls were popular (it might be remembered here that the Hilda, for instance, is marked 1914 on the back of her head) and in 1912 the lovely Schoenhut filled the pages. They were advertised as the "All Wood Perfection Art Dolls", and many of them sold for as little as $1.69, some for $2.65 and others for $2.98. The ads show them running, raising their arms, bending their knees. The beautiful doll with the molded band around her hair, so much wanted by collectors today sold under $3.00. One can easily imagine the excitement of the little girl finding these "new" dolls on the market. A doll that could really bend, and look like it was running, was unheard of!

Ads in 1930 show the Effanbee Bubbles and other Effanbee dolls. Bubbles looked most appealing in a darling drawing, wearing a big bonnet, a full ruffly dress and the sweetest grin imaginable.

The Patsy dolls were appearing, Patsy selling for $2.75. Soon to follow were the Shirley Temple dolls which led in the doll market for many years. Shirley posters, cups, buggies, dolls of all sizes, books and wardrobes were all in great demand.

Certainly to this day the Shirley doll and accessories have not lost their appeal, still being one of the most favored composition collectible items. Pictures such as those shown on the following pages were often hung on the wall of a child's bedroom, gradually filtering into the second hand stores along with the dolls, and now gracing many fine collections with their own very special appeal.

149. A group of prized Shirley posters. The two following pages are commercial photographs advertising CINDERELLA dresses.

150. Shirley Temple

151. Shirley Temple

152. Gone are the days when all these old miniatures, doll trunks and handbags can be easily found in the second hand stores. More often than not, if they do turn up, they are very high priced. But there *was* a day.....when....

BIBLIOGRAPHY

Bullard, Helen, THE AMERICAN DOLL ARTIST, Charles T. Branford Co. Boston, Mass. 1965

Coleman, Dorothy, Elizabeth & Evelyn, THE COLLECTOR'S ENCYCLOPEDIA OF DOLLS, Crown Publishers, New York. 1968

Desmonde, Kay, DOLLS & DOLLS HOUSES, The World Publishing Co., New York. 1972

Fraser, Antonia, DOLLS, Octopus Books Ltd., London, 1973

Hart, Luella, DIRECTORY OF UNITED STATES DOLL TRADEMARKS, 1888–1968.

Johl, Janet Pagter. MORE ABOUT DOLLS, Lindquist, New York, 1946.
STILL MORE ABOUT DOLLS, Lindquist, New York, 1950.
YOUR DOLLS & MINE, Lindquist, New York, 1952.

Lausanne, Edita, THE GOLDEN AGE OF TOYS, A Division of Time-Life Books, Greenwich, Connecticut, 1967.

Noble, John, DOLLS, Walker & Company, New York, 1967.

Odenrider, Ada Bridgman, WEDDING BELLES, Seattle, Washington, 1969.

INDEX

The letter p after a page number, indicates photograph.

153. Early 1900 rag dolls. Doll on left is a Horsman.   *Ethel Stewart*